はしがき

　物事を成就させるためには、その過程こそが大切です。『seek next 英語総合問題 SECOND EDITION』シリーズは、日頃の基礎固めの英語学習から、さらに受験に対応する力までを養成するために編集された総合問題集です。当シリーズは、各学習段階に応じた5冊から成り、「文法」「作文」「リスニング」「速読」「長文読解」を中心とした構成となっています。

　このシリーズの4冊目にあたる本書『seek next 4 SECOND EDITION』は、文法体系に基づく展開で、各レッスンの文法事項を軸として学習を進められるようにしています。各レッスンの「文法」の文法事項が「作文」「長文読解」へと連動しており、文法事項を確実に定着できるように工夫しています。

　また、各レッスンの「リスニング」と「速読」では、「長文読解」と同じテーマや、関連したテーマの英文を収録しています。リスニングや掲示、ウェブサイト、広告などのさまざまな読み物を通して「長文読解」の題材に関する知識を深めることができるようにしています。

本書の構成と特色

各レッスンは4ページ構成で、全部で15レッスンから成っています。各レッスンを「文法」➡「作文」➡「リスニング」➡「速読」➡「長文読解」の流れで構成しました。

■ Grammar
●必ず習得するべき重要項目を厳選し、文法体系に基づいて15レッスンに配しました。

■ Writing
●各レッスンの文法事項をふまえた部分整序作文問題もしくは英訳完成問題です。Grammarと連動した問題内容です。

■ Listening
●各レッスンの「長文読解」と同じテーマの英文を聞き取ります。
●さまざまな試験の形式に対応した問題を収録しています。
●(◀))) は、教師用付属の音声CDのトラック番号を示します。二次元コードを読み取って、音声をPCやスマートフォンなどから聞くこともできます。

■ Rapid Reading
●各レッスンの「長文読解」と同じテーマの英文を収録しています。
●ふつうの英文だけでなく、掲示、広告、メールなどの読み取り問題やグラフ問題など、さまざまな形式の問題を収録しています。

■ Reading
●各レッスンの文法事項を含んだ長文読解問題です。興味を引く題材、知的好奇心を喚起する題材、SDGsに対応した題材を選びました。
●各レッスンの「リスニング」と「速読」と同じテーマの英文を収録しています。
●速読問題：設定された時間内に本文を読み、本文の要旨や概要についての理解を問う問題としました。
●精読問題：本文の内容上の重要箇所に関する問題や文法事項を含む問題、本文全体に関する内容把握問題から成ります。

CAN-DO List
●各レッスンの学習の到達目標を「知識・技能」、「思考力・判断力・表現力」の観点から示しています。満点が取れたら、□にチェックを入れましょう。

Contents

Rapid Reading		Reading		
テーマ	問題形式			
スポーツ	GTEC®	運動靴のある工夫について。		321 words
スポーツ		トランポリンの始まりについて。		348 words
広告		国際ビジネスの注意点。	SDG 12	350 words
商業	共通テスト	アウトソーシングの問題。	SDG 10, SDG 17	348 words
言語	共通テスト	読み書きのできない親たち。	SDG 4	351 words
健康	英検®	騒音対策について。	SDG 3	380 words
商業	GTEC®	消費者の生産者に対する思い。	SDG 12	357 words
故郷	英検®	イングランド人の郷土愛。		343 words
自然	英検®	タンブルウィードについて。		369 words
ジェンダー平等	共通テスト	男性客室乗務員について。	SDG 5, SDG 8	426 words
ホームステイ	英検®	ポーランド語と英語の語彙の相違。		377 words
教育	英検®	マララ・ユスフザイの求める教育。	SDG 4, SDG 5	392 words
環境	GTEC®	世界のプラスチックごみの現状。	SDG 10, SDG 12	365 words
空港		ソマリア人が見る現代社会。		392 words
買い物		ネットショッピングについて。	SDG 12	418 words

Lesson 1 動詞

Grammar 目標➡7分

1 次の各文の( )内に下記の語群から適語を選んで補いなさい。 (各2点)

1. My brother really reminds me ( ) my father sometimes.
2. I congratulated Sue ( ) passing her driving test.
3. The sun, which is one of millions of stars in the universe, provides us ( ) heat and light.
4. He explained ( ) me how the accident had happened.
5. The soccer team blamed their coach ( ) the 3-0 defeat.

【for / of / on / to / with】

2 次の各文の( )内に入れるのに最も適当なものを選び、記号を補いなさい。 (各2点)

1. I'm very fond of this old brooch because it ( ) my grandmother.
   a. belonged　　　b. belonged to　　　c. was belonging　　　d. was belonging to
2. How long have you ( )?
   a. been married　　b. been marrying　　c. got married　　　d. married
3. My brother ( ) UFO's.
   a. believes　　　b. believes in　　　c. is believing　　　d. is believing in
4. The band ( ) a singer, two guitarists and a drummer.
   a. consists　　　b. consists of　　　c. is consisting　　　d. is consisting of

Writing 目標➡3分

3 1.～4. は( )内の語句を並べかえなさい。5.、6. は英訳しなさい。

(1～4：各3点／5、6：各5点)

1. I would like to congratulate (from / graduation / on / you / your) high school.

   _____

2. We provided (for / a helping hand / those / were / who) in need.

   _____

3. Mother blamed (Jimmy / on / on / the carpet / the mud).

   _____

4. If you're not sure about the meaning of a word, (a dictionary / in / it / look / up).

   _____

5. この歌を聞くといつも私はハワイで過ごした休暇のことを思い出します。
   This song always _____.
6. 彼は先生に遅れた理由を説明しました。

   _____

CAN-DO List □ 〈知識・技能〉動詞＋前置詞、用法を誤りやすい動詞を適切に活用できる。

4 それぞれの写真について4つの説明が読まれます。写真に最も合っているものを一つずつ選びなさい。 (各5点)

1.  ① ② ③ ④

2.  ① ② ③ ④

Rapid Reading 目標➡5分 テーマ スポーツ GTEC®

5 広告を読み取って、問いに対する答えとして最も適当なものを一つずつ選びなさい。 (各5点)

ABC Shoes ~*Now on Sale*~

SUN

Built for the all-weather runner, *Sun's MODEL 7 Running Shoes* feature their *springy cushioning and natural flexibility. They have a breathable mesh upper and a special rubber outsole which is lightweight and flexible.

STAR

Star's Maximum Running Shoes have a special midsole and also have a lightweight and *elastic outsole. Especially, this outsole grips both wet and dry surfaces. A *seamless mesh upper provides superior breathability and comfort.

ALPHA

A mesh upper gives *Alpha's Elite Running Shoes* sock-like comfort. Alpha's midsole technology provides cushioning for long-distance support. The outsole is constructed with a special rubber for slip-resistance. These men's shoes are perfect for training.

---

³springy[spríŋi]：弾力のある　⁸elastic[ɪlǽstɪk]：伸び縮みする
⁸seamless[síːmləs]：縫い目のない

1. What is the purpose of adopting a mesh-type upper?
   ① Weight saving.　② Cushioning.　③ Breathability.　④ Flexibility.

2. Making a comparison between Sun's shoes and the other two shoe makers, which of the following information is lacking in the advertisement for Sun's shoes?
   ① Midsole.　② Outsole.　③ Runner type.　④ The type of frame.

速 読問題 次の英文を2.5分で読んで、1. の問いに答えなさい。

　　Sports shoes for children, who want to run fast, are now enjoying great popularity in Japan. Children play all sorts of sports in Japanese primary and secondary schools, and every school also holds a sports day as a special school event.　Both short and long distance races are run around curved tracks in the school grounds, (1)but the *centrifugal force can make it hard to
5　stay on your feet when racing around the sharp bends on both ends of the track, and some children do slip and fall.　As a matter of fact, wearing these shoes won't make them run faster. The shoes do, however, grip firmly to the ground and that makes the children less likely to slip (2)and better able to run their best.　So why do they grip the ground so well?

　　The secret is in the *sole.　A normal grip pattern consists of *symmetrical lines which cross
10　the sole horizontally.　On these shoes, though, the lines are not *parallel, and there are rubber *studs on the soles, and they are positioned differently.　The tracks used in athletics are *regulated by *the International Association of Athletics Federations, and one of the rules is that you must run around the track *anticlockwise.　Think about what happens when you run around a bend anticlockwise.　Which parts of your feet take the most pressure?　The left
15　sides on both feet, and those places which take the most pressure are also the parts most likely to slip, and so the shoes are designed with a number of studs in (3)these important areas.　The studs are each about one millimeter long and a centimeter in diameter.　(4)They put studs on the left side of each sole, which grip the ground tightly.　The precise number varies depending on the size of the shoe.　They are placed on the outer side of the left shoe and the
20　inner side of the right shoe.　　　　　　　　　　　　　　(321 words／大阪工業大学)

---

⁴centrifugal force：遠心力　　⁹sole[sóʊl]：靴底　　⁹symmetrical[sɪmétrɪk(ə)l]：(左右)対称の
¹⁰parallel[pǽrəlèl]：平行の　　¹¹stud[stʌd]：(滑り止め)スタッド　　¹²regulate[régjəlèɪt]：…を規定する
¹²the International Association of Athletics Federations：国際陸上競技連盟
¹³anticlockwise[æ̀ntiklɑ́(:)kwaɪz]：反時計回りに

　CAN-DO List　☐ 〈知識・技能〉動詞＋前置詞、用法を誤りやすい動詞を理解できる。
　　　　　　　　☐ 〈思考力・判断力・表現力〉スポーツシューズの仕組みを的確に理解できる。

1. この英文で話題となっているスポーツシューズの靴底を表す絵として最も適当なものを、次の a.～d.から選びなさい。　　　　　　　　　　　　　　　　　　　　　　　　　（5点）

a.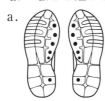
right　left

b.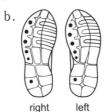
right　left

c.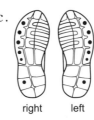
right　left

d.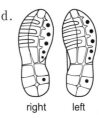
right　left

精 読問題 もう一度英文を読んで、次の問いに答えなさい。

2. 文法 下線部(1)の和訳として最も適当なものを a.～d.から一つ選びなさい。　（6点）

　　a. しかし、遠心力のせいでトラックの両端のところでぴったり止まることはむずかしく、中にはラインからずれてしまったり、転んだりする子もいる。

　　b. しかし、遠心力のせいでトラックの両端の鋭いカーブでは靴が足に強く密着し、中にはつまずいたり倒れたりする子もいる。

　　c. しかし、遠心力のせいでトラックの両端の鋭いカーブを回るときにしっかりと姿勢を保つことができなくなり、中には滑って転んでしまう子もいる。

　　d. しかし、遠心力のせいで足はトラックをはみ出してしまい、トラックの両端では大きく折れ曲がって、中には倒れ込みながらゴールする子もいる。

3. 下線部(2)の and は何と何とを結びつけていますか。それぞれを英語で答えなさい。　（8点）

4. 下線部(3)が指すものを、日本語で簡潔に説明しなさい。　　　　　　　　　　　　（9点）

5. 下線部(4)が指すものとして最も適当なものを a.～d.から一つ選びなさい。　　　（7点）

　　a. Japanese primary and secondary schools

　　b. mothers who buy their children's shoes

　　c. the children who want to run fast

　　d. the developers of these shoes

6. 全体把握 本文の内容と合っているものにはＴ、合っていないものにはＦと答えなさい。（各1点）

　　(ア) Sports shoes for children have become a great hit in Japan.　　　　　（　　　）

　　(イ) Children in Japan run around curved tracks in the school grounds every day.（　　　）

　　(ウ) Sports shoes actually make the children run faster.　　　　　　　　　（　　　）

　　(エ) The studs on the soles are all different sizes.　　　　　　　　　　　（　　　）

　　(オ) Different sizes of sports shoes have different numbers of studs.　　　（　　　）

Grammar 目標➡ 7分

1 次の各文の（　　）内に入れるのに最も適当なものを選び、記号を補いなさい。　　(各2点)

1. Something was wrong with the door; it (　　　) not open.
   a. will　　　　　b. would　　　　　c. shall　　　　　d. should

2. I wish people (　　　) drop litter in the street.
   a. don't　　　　b. shouldn't　　　c. won't　　　　d. wouldn't

3. I'm sure you are capable (　　　) the examination.
   a. for passing　b. of passing　　c. to pass　　　d. to passing

4. He looked so funny that I couldn't help (　　　).
   a. laugh　　　　b. laughing　　　c. to laugh　　　d. to laughing

5. You cannot be (　　　) careful in choosing your friends.
   a. as　　　　　b. so　　　　　　c. too　　　　　d. very

2 次の各組の文がほぼ同じ意味になるように、（　　）内に適語を補いなさい。　(各3点)

1. I should get up early tomorrow.　I have a lot to do.
   I had (　　　　　　) get up early tomorrow.　I have a lot to do.

2. His parents have good reason to be proud of him.
   His parents may (　　　　　　) be proud of him.

3. There's nothing more to do.　We'd better go home now.
   There's nothing more to do.　We might (　　　　　　) well go home now.

4. The old woman cannot take care of herself any longer.
   The old woman is (　　　　　) longer capable (　　　　　) looking after herself.

Writing 目標➡ 3分

3 （　　）内の語を並べかえて英文を完成しなさい。　　(各5点)

1. ぼくたちは、お父さんが戻るまで外出しないほうがいいよ。
   We (better / go / had / not / out) until Father comes back.

   _____

2. すみません。私がおうかがいするとあなたに電話でお知らせしておくべきでした。
   I'm sorry.　I (have / ought / phoned / to / to) tell you I was coming.

   _____

3. 映画を見に行くよりも、今夜は家にいたいわ。
   I (home / rather / stay / tonight / would) than go to the movies.

   _____

　CAN-DO List　☐ 🔊 〈知識・技能〉助動詞・助動詞に準じる表現を適切に活用できる。

4 対話を聞き、最後の発言に対する相手の応答として最も適当なものを一つずつ選びなさい。

（各5点）

1. ①　②　③　④
2. ①　②　③　④

Rapid Reading   目標➡ 5分   テーマ スポーツ

5 （1）・（2）に入れるのに最も適当なものを一つずつ選びなさい。　（各5点）

Trampolining

　Trampolining is one type of gymnastics. It uses just one piece of equipment; a trampoline. It consists of a sheet of strong material which is attached by springs to a frame. Basically, the only thing the performers do is jump on this trampoline. Competitive trampolining consists of simple jumps, rotations, twists etc.　Performances are judged using a 10-point scale. The scoring （　1　） of competitive trampolining are similar to those of gymnastics.　So, in competitive trampolining the players perform the actions like （　2　）. Trampolining became an official Olympic sport in the 2000 Sydney Olympics.　Since then many countries have started adopting trampolining.

1. ① equipment　② positions　③ terms　④ criteria
2. ① astronaut　② diving　③ racing　④ acrobatics

□ 🎧 〈思考力・判断力・表現力〉相手の発言を聞いて的確な応答ができる。
□ 📖 〈思考力・判断力・表現力〉トランポリンについての簡単な説明を完成できる。

Lesson 2 ｜ 9

Reading 目標⇒20分 文法項目 助動詞に準ずる表現 テーマ スポーツ 7

速読問題 次の英文を2.5分で読んで、1. の問いに答えなさい。

Across the UK you now find trampolines in many homes. Market research shows that trampolines are the third most-wanted gift for children. To (1)meet this demand, *retailers are rushing to enter the trampoline market.

Trampoline manufacturers are fond of saying that the *Eskimos created the first
5 trampolines when they used stretched *walrus skins to toss each other high up into the air. However, stretching material to toss people up into the air is not unique to Eskimos. Many cultures have a folk tradition of tossing people by a blanket for fun or as a form of celebration. In Europe (2)this activity gradually developed into a form of public entertainment when touring entertainment groups added a "jumping bed" act to their performances. The "bed"
10 consisted of strong canvas stretched over a frame covered with bed clothes, and allowed performers to add a huge range of visually amusing moves to their standard comedy acts.

In any case, circus tradition recognizes the French showman Du Trampolin as the inventor of (3)the large-scale, fine net trampoline that we are familiar with today. Du Trampolin noticed that some *trapeze artists used the safety net underneath their swings to end their act
15 by jumping down to the ground in an elegant way. Du Trampolin experimented with various combinations of net and frame design to find the best way of providing lift and control to allow the entertainer to safely jump and twist through the air. The entertainer George Nissen took Du Trampolin's basic designs a stage further in the 1930s. Working in his garage at home, Nissen created a trampoline on which performers were able to show off their diving and
20 rolling skills. These shows caught the attention of serious sports coaches and athletes. From this modest start, trampolining as we know it today spread around the world.

But (4)trampolining is more than just a recreational sport. In the 1960s, American astronauts trained on trampolines to practice variable body positions in space flight. And in general, trampolining offers a very healthy form of intense physical exercise without
25 unnecessary stress on your bones and joints. (348 words / 甲南大学)

---

² retailer[rí:tèɪlər]：小売業者　⁴ Eskimo[éskɪmòʊ]：エスキモー（ツンドラ地帯に住む先住民族。蔑称とされ、現在では Inuit と呼称することがふつう）　⁵ walrus[wɔ́:lrəs]：セイウチ
¹⁴ trapeze artist：空中ブランコ曲芸師

CAN-DO List ☐ 〈知識・技能〉助動詞・助動詞に準ずる表現を理解できる。
☐ 〈思考力・判断力・表現力〉トランポリンの歴史と現状について的確に理解できる。

1. この英文のタイトルとして最も適当なものを、次の a.～ d. から選びなさい。　　　（5点）

   a．Effects of Trampolining on Health　　　b．The History of the Trampoline

   c．Trampolining as a Recreational Sport　　　d．Trampolining as a Serious Sport

精 読問題 もう一度英文を読んで、次の問いに答えなさい。

2. 下線部(1)の意味として最も適当なものを a.～ d. から一つ選びなさい。　　　（7点）

   a．experience　　　b．join　　　c．look at　　　d．satisfy

3. 下線部(2)が指すものを、英語で答えなさい。　　　（8点）

_____

4. 下線部(3)の原形となったものは何ですか。日本語で説明しなさい。　　　（8点）

_____

5. **文法** 下線部(4)の意味として最も適当なものを a.～ d. から一つ選びなさい。　　　（7点）

   a．We cannot be too careful when we use trampolines for recreational purposes.

   b．Trampolining is expected to become a higher level recreational sport.

   c．Trampolining as a sport is nothing more than recreation.

   d．Trampolining offers more than mere recreation.

6. **全体把握** 第1、第2パラグラフの内容と合っているものを、a.～ f. から二つ選び、記号で答えなさい。　　　（各2点）

   a．According to market research, there are three times as many trampolines in the UK as other gifts for children.

   b．Trampoline manufacturers firmly believe that the Eskimos invented the trampoline in order to stretch walrus skins.

   c．Many manufacturers in the UK began to produce trampolines right after they saw Eskimos throwing each other into the air using walrus skins.

   d．The use of stretched material to throw people into the air has been observed in many cultures.

   e．Many performers in Europe used to toss beds into the air on stage after it was established as a comedy act.

   f．The use of a "jumping bed" enabled performers to extend the range of their comic actions.

7. **全体把握** 第3、第4パラグラフの内容と合っているものを、a.～ e. から二つ選び、記号で答えなさい。　　　（各2点）

   a．It is commonly assumed that the first trampoline was created by an Eskimo called Du Trampolin.

   b．Du Trampolin borrowed landing devices for the trapeze artists to use as a safety net.

   c．George Nissen's designs were further developed by Du Trampolin to show off his diving skills.

   d．George Nissen's trampoline was used by performers to demonstrate their skills, which impressed sports coaches and athletes.

   e．Trampolines were used to prepare astronauts for space missions.

Lesson 3 受動態

Grammar　目標➡ 7分

1 次の各文の（　　）内に下記の語群から適語を選んで補いなさい。 (各2点)

1. The movie is based (　　　　) a true story.
2. That singer is known (　　　　) everyone in the country.
3. I'm not satisfied (　　　　) the result.
4. The sweater she wore was made (　　　　) wool.
5. An icicle is made (　　　　) dripping water that freezes.
6. The members of the marching band were dressed (　　　　) red and white.
7. He was so surprised (　　　　) the news that he couldn't say a single word.

【at / from / in / of / on / to / with】

2 下線部を主語にした受動態の文を完成しなさい。 (各4点)

1. It is thought that the number 13 is a sign of bad luck.

   The number 13 is thought _____.

2. It was said that Mars had many man-made channels on the surface.

   Mars was said _____.

3. It is said that the earth was part of the sun.

   The earth is said _____.

Writing　目標➡ 3分

3 1.～3. は（　　）内の語句を並べかえなさい。4.、5. は英訳しなさい。

(1～3：各3点／4、5：各5点)

1. Consumers should complain if they are not (receive / satisfied / the service / they / with).

   _____

2. The walls of her room are (covered / of / pop stars / pictures / with).

   _____

3. Please pack these things very carefully. I don't want them (get / damaged / to).

   _____

4. 彼の年齢は正確にはわかっていないが、108歳だと言われている。

   Nobody knows exactly how old he is, but _____.

5. この道路は古代ローマ人が作ったものだと言われている。

   _____ by the Romans.

CAN-DO List　□　〈知識・技能〉by 以外の前置詞を用いる受動態、They say that ... の受動態を適切に活用できる。

4 英文を聞き、□1□〜□4□の空所に合うものを①〜④から一つずつ選びなさい。　（各2点）

Sales Trends of the Advertising Market

| 1 | ( ) | 2 | ( ) | 3 | ( ) | 4 | ( ) |

① TV　　　　　　　　　　　　　② Transportation advertisement
③ Newspaper inserts and direct mail　　④ Internet advertisement

Rapid Reading　目標➡5分　　　　　　　　テーマ 広告

5 記事を読み取って、問いに対する答えとして最も適当なものを一つずつ選びなさい。　（各5点）

99.9% Approval & 100% Satisfaction!

MM2H (Malaysia My Second Home) Program is promoted by the Government of Malaysia. By taking advantage of this program, you are allowed to stay in Malaysia as long as possible. It is open to people from all over the world who fulfill certain criteria, regardless of race, religion, gender or age. So, it is now attracting foreign people to Malaysia not only so they can enjoy staying after retirement but also so they can use it as a base for such things as conducting business and educating their children.

We can help you to obtain this long term visa in a legal way within one to one and a half months. The MM2H visa permit is initially for ten years and is renewable.

Faisal Consultancy
☎ *+60123456789*
✉ faisalconsultancy@seekmail.com

1. What kind of company is Faisal Consultancy?

　① Agent　　　　　② Developer　　　　③ Insurance Company　④ Trading Company

2. Which of the following statements is true?

　① The moment we apply for MM2H Program, we can obtain the visa.
　② It is possible for the people who participate in MM2H Program to stay in Malaysia for over 10 years.
　③ There are no restrictions on participation in MM2H Program.
　④ All the applicants who applied for MM2H Program through Faisal Consultancy have been able to obtain the visa.

Reading　目標➡20分　文法項目 by 以外の前置詞を用いる受動態　テーマ 商業　🔊 9

速 読問題 次の英文を2.5分で読んで、1. の問いに答えなさい。

When promoting a product around the world, it benefits companies to understand local customs in detail.　Knowing what appeals to potential customers, as well as knowledge about the *"do's and don'ts" of each market, can help a product be successful.

When it comes to the name of the product, the most important thing to consider is the local
5 language.　(1)It may seem obvious, but companies often make mistakes.　For example, Coca Cola tried to write their name in Chinese as 蝌蚪啃蠟 (Ke-kou-ke-la).　However, they soon found out this meant "Bite The Wax *Tadpole."　Of course, this sounded so silly that the company had to take down all the posters!　(2)The name was later changed into more appropriate Chinese characters (可口可樂) meaning, "The more you drink, the more fun you
10 will have."

There are other things to (3)think about, too.　Different traditions mean that even simple things like colors or numbers can affect the success of a product.　For example, in some cultures there are unlucky colors, such as black in Japan or white in China.　There are also some numbers which are thought to be unlucky.　Many hotels in the USA or the UK do not
15 have a room 13 or 13th floor.　Japanese airlines do not have the seat numbers 4 or 9.　It would be very unwise to use these unlucky colors or numbers in your product or advertising.

Finally, different cultures have different concepts of relationships between men and women.　It may make (4)certain pictures unsuitable for some cultures.　For example, though it is common to see pictures of couples kissing each other on posters in the USA, (5)such images
20 would make *Muslims in the Middle East very embarrassed.

Even when a product is the same, its sales success depends on how appropriately and effectively it appeals to people in different countries.　Knowing such things is *the golden rule of doing global business.　So when preparing to do business in a foreign country, you should investigate the language and customs there.　An American president once said
25 that (6)the money you earn depends on the knowledge you learn in life.　(350 words / 近畿大学)

---

3 do's and don'ts：すべきこととしてはいけないこと、慣行　　7 tadpole[tǽdpòul]：オタマジャクシ
20 Muslim[mázlɪm]：イスラム教徒　22 the golden rule：ゴールデンルール（行動の基本原理）

　CAN-DO List　☐ 〈知識・技能〉by 以外の前置詞を用いる受動態を理解できる。
　　　　　　　☐ 〈思考力・判断力・表現力〉海外でのビジネス展開の留意点を的確に理解できる。

1. この英文の5つのパラグラフを内容の面から三つに分けたとき、その分け方として最も適当なものを、次のa.～d.から選びなさい。 （5点）

   a. 第1パラグラフ／第2・第3パラグラフ／第4・第5パラグラフ

   b. 第1パラグラフ／第2～第4パラグラフ／第5パラグラフ

   c. 第1・第2パラグラフ／第3パラグラフ／第4・第5パラグラフ

   d. 第1・第2パラグラフ／第3・第4パラグラフ／第5パラグラフ

精 読問題 もう一度英文を読んで、次の問いに答えなさい。

2. 下線部⑴のItの具体的な内容を、日本語で説明しなさい。 （6点）

---

3. 文法 下線部⑵を和訳しなさい。 （5点）

---

4. 下線部⑶とほぼ同じ内容を表している1語を、本文中から抜き出しなさい。 （5点）

---

5. 下線部⑷の具体例を、本文中から抜き出しなさい。 （5点）

---

6. 下線部⑸と同じ文型の文をa.～d.から一つ選びなさい。 （3点）

   a. Mother made us cheese sandwiches for lunch.

   b. Mrs. Johnson makes her living by writing books.

   c. The story of his adventures makes fascinating reading.

   d. We made the house more secure by putting locks on the window.

7. 下線部⑹の意味として最も適当なものをa.～d.から一つ選びなさい。 （3点）

   a. How much you learn in your lifetime is affected by the amount of money you earn.

   b. The knowledge you learn in life is more important than the money you earn.

   c. The money you earn is compared to the knowledge you learn in life.

   d. What you learn during your lifetime determines the wealth that you are able to acquire.

8. 全体把握 本文の内容と合っているものにはT、合っていないものにはFと答えなさい。 （各1点）

  (ア) 世界に製品を売り込むためには、それぞれの地域のビジネスのし方に従いさえすればよい。

                                 （   ）

  (イ) 地域の言語を不用意に用いて失敗を犯す企業もある。 （   ）

  (ウ) 地域によって製品や広告に使用するのを避けるべき色や数字もある。 （   ）

  (エ) 人々を不快にさせるものは、世界共通である。 （   ）

  (オ) 世界にビジネスを展開するためには、その製品の規格や品質が一定していなくてはならない。

                                   （   ）

Lesson 4 to-不定詞

Grammar 目標➡ 7分

1 次の各文の（　　）内に入れるのに最も適当なものを選び、記号を補いなさい。　　　　（各2点）

1. *A* : I heard you were invited to the President's party.

   B : Yes.　I was surprised at how easy the President was (　　　).
   a. for talking　　　　b. talking to　　　　c. to talk　　　　d. to talk to

2. Where (　　　) the typhoon most likely to hit?
   a. are　　　　　　　b. do　　　　　　　　c. does　　　　　　d. is

3. I hear you've been dating a beautiful girl lately.　How did you (　　　) to know her?
   a. become　　　　　b. come　　　　　　　c. go　　　　　　　d. is

4. I'm not used to this computer.　Do you (　　　) to know a person who could tell me how to use it?
   a. happen　　　　　b. manage　　　　　　c. see　　　　　　　d. want

5. He was made (　　　) it against his will.
   a. do　　　　　　　b. doing　　　　　　　c. done　　　　　　d. to do

6. She was seen (　　　) into the theater with her boyfriend.
   a. go　　　　　　　b. went　　　　　　　c. gone　　　　　　d. to go

7. Two people are reported to (　　　) in an explosion at a factory in Miami early this morning.
   a. be injured　　　b. injure　　　　　　c. have been injured　d. have injured

Writing 目標➡ 3分

2 1.〜3. は（　　）内の語句を並べかえなさい。4.、5. は英訳しなさい。

（1〜3：各4点／4、5：各5点）

1. 近頃の子供は昔の子供ほど喜ばせるのは簡単でない。

   Children today are (as / as / easy / not / please / to) they were in the past.

   _____

2. 自分自身の欠点に気づかない人は他人を非難しがちである。

   A man (is / to / apt / blind / his own faults) to criticize others.

   _____

3. Men are (die / from / likely / more / to) heart attacks than women.

   _____

4. 私は食事を終えるたびごとに両親に歯をみがかされました。

   I was made by my parents _____ .

5. ひょっとして、あなたは私の友人のジョン・スミスをご存知ではありませんか。

   _____

CAN-DO List □ 〈知識・技能〉いろいろな to- 不定詞の文を適切に活用できる。

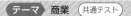
3 話を聞き、示された条件に最も合うものを、①〜④から一つ選びなさい。下の表を参考にしてメモを取ってもかまいません。 （6点）

状況
あなたは、デパートのバイヤーとしてTシャツを仕入れようと思います。4社のTシャツメーカーからそれぞれの特徴を聞いています。

あなたが考えている条件
A. 品質がよいこと
B. フェアトレードに関連した製品であること
C. 価格は一枚20ドル程度と、高すぎないこと

T-shirt	Condition A	Condition B	Condition C
① VELVA TEE			
② WAREHOUSE T-shirts			
③ UG T-shirts			
④ CHAMP T-shirts			

☐ is the T-shirts you are most likely to choose.
　① VELVA TEE　　② WAREHOUSE　　③ UG T-shirts　　④ CHAMP

Rapid Reading 目標➡5分　テーマ 商業 共通テスト

4 以下のウェブサイトに掲載された学校の先生たちのフェアトレードに関するコメントを読み取って、問いに対する答えとして最も適当なものを一つずつ選びなさい。 （各5点）

Comments on Fair-Trade Products	
Mr. Tamura	Bananas are one of the most popular fruits in the world. Therefore, the higher the sales, the more the profits increase for producers. We should make sure the profits made by fair trade directly go to the suppliers and producers.
Ms. Ishibashi	Chocolate is one of the world's most popular snacks. Did you know what chocolate is made from? Cacao is the plant behind chocolate. I believe the cacao business should be changed because this business is related to widespread poverty, deforestation, gender inequality and child labor.
Ms. Nakano	Over 125 million people depend on coffee for making their living. However, many of them are unable to support their family members. In order to improve this situation, why don't you try fair-trade coffee, so that the coffee farmers can grow better quality beans and lead a better life?

1. One fact from the teachers' individual comments on Fair Trade is that " ☐1 "
　① There are more than 125 million people working for the production of coffee.
　② All the teachers are responsible for advertising fair-trade products.
　③ More profits will be made from fair-trade bananas.
　④ Bananas and cacao are the most popular products in the world.

2. One opinion from the teachers' comments is that " ☐2 "
　① Mr. Tamura thinks that the profits made through fair trade should be received by the farmers and suppliers.
　② Ms. Ishibashi believes that the cacao business should remain the same because it is really popular in the world.
　③ Ms. Nakano says we should try fair-trade coffee because it is so delicious and high-quality.
　④ All the teachers agree that fair-trade products should make more money than they do now.

Reading 目標➡20分 文法項目 いろいろな to-不定詞 テーマ 商業   11

速 読問題 次の英文を2.5分で読んで、1. の問いに答えなさい。

The world's consumption of fashion is huge. (1)To give just one example, the United States alone imported more than 126 billion dollars' worth of *textiles in 2015. As consumption has risen, prices have fallen. Today, a hand-finished shirt may cost as little as five dollars. ァTo make clothes at these low prices, companies have ィto keep costs down. They use *offshore
5 production to do this. Large multinational companies *outsource their production to developing countries like Egypt or Cambodia, where workers are paid much less than in developed countries. Supporters of outsourcing claim that it helps local economies, but I believe it is harmful for two main reasons.

First, overseas workers usually receive very low wages. (2)These workers, many of them
10 women and children, often work 14 hours a day and earn less than a hundred dollars a month. One study of 15 countries found that textile workers earned less than 40% of the money they needed ゥto live on each month. In some countries this figure is even lower. Such low wages are wrong and unfair.

The second problem with outsourcing is that working conditions in many offshore factories
15 are uncomfortable and unsafe. It is a fact that worker protection laws like those in developed nations either don't exist or (3)often are not followed. As a result, workers are exposed to chemicals, dust, and horrible accidents happen.

I realize some experts, like the economist David Schneider, say that outsourcing benefits local economies by providing jobs at higher wages than local workers can make by working in
20 agriculture. Supporters of outsourcing point out that people in developing countries often line up (4)to take jobs in multinational factories. These arguments may be correct, but in my opinion they do not justify the low wages and dangerous working conditions found in many overseas factories today. If multinationals are going to continue ェto benefit from low production costs by using overseas suppliers, I believe they should contribute a much larger
25 share of their massive profits to correcting (5)these problems and improving social conditions in the countries where they are located——starting today. (348 words / 京都文教大学)

---

² textile [tékstaɪl]：繊維製品   ⁴ offshore [ɔ̀ːʃɔ́ːr]：海外 (で) の
⁵ outsource [áʊtsɔ̀ːrs]：…を外部発注 [委託] する

CAN-DO List ☐ 〈知識・技能〉いろいろな to- 不定詞を理解できる。
☐ 〈思考力・判断力・表現力〉生産拠点を海外に移す際の留意点を的確に理解できる。

1. この英文のタイトルとして最も適当なものを、次のa.～d.から選びなさい。 （5点）

a. アウトソーシングをめぐる海外工場の議論と問題点

b. 大企業の海外移転がもたらす利点

c. 農業労働者と工場労働者が抱える問題点

d. 発展途上国と先進国の間に存在する賃金格差の問題

精 読問題 もう一度英文を読んで、次の問いに答えなさい。

2. 下線部(1)の具体例として挙げられているものはどのようなものか、[　]内に適語を入れ日本文を完成しなさい。 （各3点）

[①　　　　　　　]年には[②　　　　　　]で[③　　　　　　]億ドル分以上の繊維製品を[④　　　　　]しています。

3. 下線部(2)は具体的にはどのような人がどのような状況で働かされていますか。[　]内に適語を入れ日本語で説明しなさい。 （5点）

[　　　　　　　　　　　　　　　　　　　　　　　　　] 状況で働かされている。

4. 下線部(3)の意味として最も適当なものを、次のa.～d.から選びなさい。 （5点）

a. 検討すらされていないことが多い。

b. 存在すら知られていないことが多い。

c. 順守されていないことが多い。

d. 立ち入り調査すら行われていないことが多い。

5. **文法** 下線部(4)のto-不定詞と同じ用法のものを本文中のア～エから選びなさい。 （5点）

6. 下線部(5)が指すものは何ですか。海外工場で起きている主な問題を2つ、本文の内容に即して、[　]内に適語を入れ日本語で述べなさい。 （各5点）

① [　　　　　　　　　　]で働くこと。　　② [　　　　　　　　　　]で働くこと。

7. **全体把握** 本文の内容と合っていないものを、次のa.～e.から一つ選びなさい。 （6点）

a. 衣料の値段を抑えようとすると、企業はコストダウンを続けなければならない。

b. 大規模な多国籍企業は、エジプトやカンボジアなどの発展途上国に生産を委託している。

c. 15か国を対象にしたある調査では、繊維産業の労働者が毎月の生活に必要なお金の40%未満しか稼いでいないという結果が出ている。

d. 経済学者のデビッド・シュナイダーは、外国資本の工場労働者よりも地元の農業労働者のほうがはるかに高収入だと主張している。

e. 筆者は多国籍企業が得た利益は海外工場がある国々が抱える問題を解決するために使うべきだと主張している。

Lesson 5 動名詞

Grammar 目標➡7分

1 次の各組の文がほぼ同じ意味になるように、(　　　)内に適語を補いなさい。 (各3点)

1. We couldn't go out because of the bad weather.

   The bad weather (　　　　　) us (　　　　　) going out.

2. I'm in no mood to cook tonight.

   I don't feel (　　　　　) cooking tonight.

3. It is useless to ask her a little favor.

   It is no (　　　　　) (　　　　　) her a little favor.

4. It is impossible to tell what she will do next.

   There is (　　　　　) (　　　　　) what she will do next.

2 次の各文の(　　　)内に入れるのに最も適当なものを選び、記号を補いなさい。 (各2点)

1. He denied (　　　　　) money from the cash register.

   a. having taken　　b. himself to take　　c. to take　　d. to have taken

2. She went out of the room without (　　　　) by anyone present there.

   a. being noticed　　b. noticing　　c. be noticed　　d. to be noticed

3. This book is well worth (　　　　).

   a. read　　b. for reading　　c. in reading　　d. reading

4. It was a (　　　　) of time going to see that film; it was very boring.

   a. change　　b. matter　　c. use　　d. waste

Writing 目標➡3分

3 1.～3.は(　　　)内の語句を並べかえなさい。4.、5.は英訳しなさい。

(1～3：各3点／4、5：各5点)

1. I'm already eighteen years old now.　I (a / being / child / hate / like / really / treated).

   _____

2. いつこの地域に激しい地震があるかはだれにもわからない。

   There (when / knowing / a severe earthquake / no / is / will happen) in this area.

   _____

3. 私は自分の気持ちを言葉にするのがあまり得意ではない。

   I'm (putting / feelings / good / not / very / at / my) into words.

   _____

4. 雨が降って、私たちはテニスができませんでした。

   The rain _____.

5. これ以上ジョンを待ってもむだです。

   _____ any longer.

CAN-DO List ☐ 〈知識・技能〉動名詞を含む慣用表現、いろいろな動名詞を適切に活用できる。

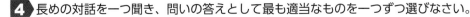

4 長めの対話を一つ聞き、問いの答えとして最も適当なものを一つずつ選びなさい。 （各5点）

1. When did the man begin to learn English?

　① Before he went to elementary school.

　② In the third year of elementary school.

　③ In the fifth year of elementary school.

　④ When he was a junior high school student.

2. What will the woman do after this conversation?

　① She will send an e-mail to her friend living in the US.

　② She will be given the man's e-mail address.

　③ She will begin to exchange e-mails with the man.

　④ She will go to Taiwan with the man.

Rapid Reading 目標➡5分 テーマ 言語 共通テスト

5 グラフを読み取って、問いに対する答えとして最も適当なものを一つずつ選びなさい。 （各5点）

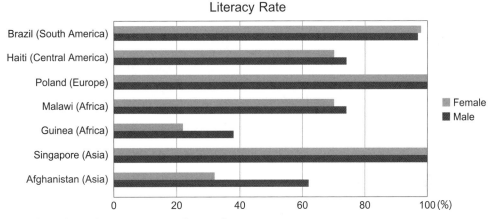

Literacy Rate

1. Which of the following statements is true?

　① There is no country where the male literacy rate is a higher percentage than the female literacy rate.

　② The difference in the literacy rate between females and males in Guinea and Afghanistan is almost double.

　③ The percentage pattern in the literacy rate between Haiti and Malawi is different.

　④ No other country has a lower percentage than Afghanistan in the literacy rate.

2. Which of the following statements is best supported by the above graph?

　① There are a lot of immigrants in Brazil.

　② Poland is more advanced than any other country in English education.

　③ Singapore is a multi-ethnic nation.

　④ The females of Afghanistan aren't given enough education, compared with the males of Afghanistan.

CAN-DO List ☐ 〈思考力・判断力・表現力〉対話の内容から今後を推測し的確な判断ができる。

☐ 〈思考力・判断力・表現力〉グラフから、必要な情報を読み取ることができる。 **Lesson 5** 21

Reading　目標➡20分　文法項目 いろいろな動名詞　テーマ 教育・言語　◀))) 13

速読問題 次の英文を2.5分で読んで、1. の問いに答えなさい。

　　Adults in America tend to hide reading difficulties if they have them. They are embarrassed by the fact that they have not mastered basic literacy skills, and many are good at keeping this fact concealed from employers, employees, and their relatives; others are not capable of (1)maintaining such a false face. This problem is deeply personal to me because I

5　recently discovered that some of my oldest and dearest relatives had difficulty reading. (2)They had managed to keep this hidden from me for most of my life. It was my personal experience that loving adults would pretend to read stories to me as a child, which is why I thought they could read. These older relatives would present a flowing story to me as if they were actually fluent readers. Since I was too young to know the difference, I simply

10　assumed that they could read, which was the objective of their loving pretense. (3)The essential point is simple though, and worth repeating. If parents cannot read, they will not be able to teach their children to read, or to monitor the development of their children's literacy. Some poor parents have developed unique strategies to cope with this serious problem; they locate tutors for their children and follow the suggestions offered by those tutors.

15　These parents clearly want their children to receive a good education even though they do not have the personal literacy skills to lend direct assistance. By banding together with other parents who share similar concerns and then hiring qualified educational advisers to help them and their children, some parents have adopted very creative strategies to improve educational prospects for their children. (4)Whenever their children bring home *memoranda

20　from school, the parents contact their advisers, who then read the documents and offer their best advice on how the parents should proceed. (5)This situation is not typical; few *inner-city parents, either alone or as a group, have the financial resources to hire such advisers. Nevertheless, many minority parents have *gone to extraordinary lengths to secure educational support for their children even though they themselves have not yet mastered

25　literacy.

(351 words / 青山学院大学)

CAN-DO List　□ 〈知識・技能〉動名詞を含む慣用表現、いろいろな動名詞の文を理解できる。
　　　　　　　　□ 〈思考力・判断力・表現力〉アメリカ人の識字率と子の教育への熱心さの関係を的確に理解できる。

¹⁹ memoranda[mèmərǽndə]：memorandum（連絡通知表）の複数形　²¹ inner-city：都心の低所得者密集地区
の　²³ go to extraordinary lengths to ～：～するためにはどんなことでもする

1. この英文は全体として何について述べていますか。次の a.～ d.から選びなさい。　　　　（5点）
　　a. 合衆国に読み書きのできない大人が多い社会的背景
　　b. 読み書きのできない親たちの子供の教育にかける熱意
　　c. 読み書きのできない親たちはその事実を子供たちにどのように隠しているか
　　d. 読み書きのできない親に対する子供たちの複雑な思い

精 読問題 もう一度英文を読んで、次の問いに答えなさい。

2. 文法 下線部(1)の具体的な内容を、日本語で説明しなさい。　　　　　　　　　　　　（5点）

3. 下線部(2)を和訳しなさい。　　　　　　　　　　　　　　　　　　　　　　　　　　（7点）

4. 文法 下線部(3)の The essential point の具体的な内容を、日本語で説明しなさい。　　（6点）

5. 下線部(4)を和訳しなさい。　　　　　　　　　　　　　　　　　　　　　　　　　　（6点）

6. 下線部(5)の理由を、日本語で説明しなさい。　　　　　　　　　　　　　　　　　　（5点）

7. 全体把握 本文の内容と合っているものにはＴ、合っていないものにはＦと答えなさい。（各1点）
　(ア) Adults in America who have reading difficulties tend to keep the fact concealed.
　　　　　　　　　　　　　　　　　　　　　　　　　　　　　　　　　　　　（　　　）
　(イ) People with reading difficulties can never keep the fact hidden for a long time.
　　　　　　　　　　　　　　　　　　　　　　　　　　　　　　　　　　　　（　　　）
　(ウ) The author's older relatives would actually read stories to him as a child.　They were
　　　 very good readers.　　　　　　　　　　　　　　　　　　　　　　　　　（　　　）
　(エ) Even if parents cannot read, they will be able to monitor the development of their
　　　 children's literacy.　　　　　　　　　　　　　　　　　　　　　　　　　（　　　）
　(オ) It is clear that the parents who cannot read want their children to receive a good
　　　 education.　　　　　　　　　　　　　　　　　　　　　　　　　　　　　（　　　）
　(カ) Some parents with reading difficulties band together with other parents who can read.
　　　　　　　　　　　　　　　　　　　　　　　　　　　　　　　　　　　　（　　　）
　(キ) Many inner-city parents do not have enough money to hire qualified educational
　　　 advisers.　　　　　　　　　　　　　　　　　　　　　　　　　　　　　（　　　）

Lesson 6 分詞

Grammar 目標➡7分

1 次の各文の（　　）内に入れるのに最も適当なものを選び、記号を補いなさい。 （各2点）

1. (　　　) in Paris for five years, he speaks French as if he were a Frenchman.
   - a. Being staying
   - b. Having been stayed
   - c. Having stayed
   - d. Stayed

2. The young actor, (　　　) forgotten his lines, stood motionless on the stage.
   - a. because
   - b. being
   - c. having
   - d. he has

3. Not (　　　) what to do, I telephoned the police.
   - a. being known
   - b. to know
   - c. knowing
   - d. known

4. All things (　　　), I'm sure we made the right decision.
   - a. go on
   - b. to compare
   - c. getting difficult
   - d. considered

5. Jim is 65, but he isn't going to retire yet.　He wants to (　　　) on working.
   - a. bring
   - b. come
   - c. go
   - d. take

6. Rita and Howard are busy (　　　) arrangements for their wedding.
   - a. make
   - b. making
   - c. to be making
   - d. to make

7. John and I went for a walk.　I had trouble (　　　) up with him because he was walking so fast.
   - a. keeping
   - b. putting
   - c. to keep
   - d. to put

8. *A* : What did you do last night?
   B : Oh, nothing special.　I spent most of the evening (　　　) TV.
   - a. seeing
   - b. to see
   - c. to watch
   - d. watching

Writing 目標➡3分

2 1.～3. は（　　）内の語句を並べかえなさい。4.、5. は英訳しなさい。

（1～3：各3点／4、5：各5点）

1. Having (all / money / nearly / our / spent), we couldn't afford to stay in a hotel.

2. Not (able / being / English / to / understand), the man didn't know what I wanted.

3. We spent (about / most / of / talking / the evening) our vacation.

4. 母は、明日のパーティーの準備でてんてこ舞いしています。

5. 私たちは、彼の家を見つけるのに少し手間取りました。

CAN-DO List □ 〈知識・技能〉分詞を使った慣用表現、いろいろな分詞構文を適切に活用できる。

3 英語の質問と、それに対する応答が 4 つ読まれます。応答として最も適当なものを一つずつ選び
なさい。　　　　　　　　　　　　　　　　　　　　　　　　　　　　　　　　　（各 5 点）

1. ① ② ③ ④　　　　　　　　　　　　2. ① ② ③ ④

Rapid Reading　目標➡ 5 分　　　　　　　　　　テーマ 健康　英検®

4（1）・（2）に入れるのに最も適当なものを一つずつ選びなさい。　　　（各 5 点）

　　I live close to the station.　It's convenient, but it also causes a big problem.　In the summer I have to choose between (　1　).　If I have the windows open for a breath of fresh air, there's a terrible noise every time a train passes.　I can't listen to music or watch TV for more than ten minutes without being interrupted.　If I close the window, though, the room gets too hot and I feel like (　2　).

1. ① hearing and breathing
　② hearing and sleeping
　③ seeing and breathing
　④ sleeping and seeing
2. ① I need a good night's sleep
　② I need a little peace and quiet
　③ I need more air
　④ I need more light

Reading 目標➡20分　文法項目 分詞を使った慣用表現　テーマ 健康　 16

速 読問題 次の英文を2.5分で読んで、1. の問いに答えなさい。

Loud noises can affect your hearing. They can cause ear pain. Even worse, if sound waves from very loud noises reach your inner ear, they can *rip and tear *tissues needed for hearing.

Often ears will heal themselves if they are not hurt too badly. There may only be a short
5 time after the loud noise that you cannot hear. But hearing can be lost forever if the damage is very bad. Or hearing may be damaged so that you may hear (1)some sounds, but not (2)others. For example, you may be able to hear a car horn, but have trouble hearing someone speaking.

It is a sad fact, but the world is getting noisier. Noise is just about everywhere. Yet, our
10 world could be made quieter. Every effort should be made to do away with loud noise. Our health depends upon it.

One way to cut down on noise is to quiet the thing that makes the noise. For instance, mufflers on car exhaust pipes cut down the amount of noise a car makes. Without mufflers you could hardly (3)stand the noise of your own car. That is one reason why mufflers are
15 important.

Noise can also be stopped in other ways. One way is to soak up noise. Sound waves bounce off walls and ceilings in rooms. Their echoes add to the new sounds in the rooms. (4)Ceilings made of tiles with little holes in them take in sound waves much as sponges soak up water. This cuts room noise down quite a bit. Carpets, curtains, and furniture also
20 soak up sound waves. It is a fact that an empty room is full of echoes. A room with furniture is much quieter. (5)Putting machines on rubber pads can cut down noise by keeping tables and floors from shaking along with the machines. Their shaking adds to the noise from the machines.

Noise can also be blocked or stopped completely. That might seem like the best way to
25 stop noise, but (6)it is not always so. For example, *soundproof rooms mean that walls and ceilings must be very thick and covered with soundproofing material. The extra building materials would make homes and apartments more expensive. Cheaper and easier ways to cut down on unwanted noise need to be developed.

(380 words / 甲南大学)

²rip [ríp]：…を（びりっと引き）裂く　²tissue [tíʃuː]：膜、組織　²⁵soundproof [sáundprùːf]：防音の

| **CAN-DO List** ☐ 🔵 〈知識・技能〉分詞を使った慣用表現、いろいろな分詞構文の文を理解できる。
☐ 🔴 〈思考力・判断力・表現力〉騒音と防音対策の話の展開を的確に理解できる。

1. この英文のタイトルとして最も適当なものを、次のa.～d.から選びなさい。　　　　（5点）

   a. 現代の都市生活における騒音公害

   b. さまざまな騒音対策とその効果

   c. 騒音の人体に対する影響と騒音対策のあれこれ

   d. 騒音の人体に対する深刻な影響

精 読問題 もう一度英文を読んで、次の問いに答えなさい。

2. 下線部(1)の具体例を、本文中から抜き出しなさい。　　　　　　　　　　　（5点）

_____

3. 文法 下線部(2)の具体例を、本文中から抜き出しなさい。　　　　　　　（5点）

_____

4. 下線部(3)とほぼ同じ意味を表すものをa.～d.から一つ選びなさい。　　　（4点）

   a. cut down on　　　b. do away with　　　c. get along with　　　d. put up with

5. 下線部(4)を和訳しなさい。　　　　　　　　　　　　　　　　　　　　　（7点）

_____

_____

6. 下線部(5)の理由を、日本語で説明しなさい。　　　　　　　　　　　　　（7点）

_____

7. 下線部(6)を、itとsoの具体的な内容を明らかにして、和訳しなさい。　　（8点）

_____

8. 全体把握 本文の内容と合っていないものを、a.～g.から二つ選び、記号で答えなさい。（各2点）

   a. Loud noise may lead to loss of hearing.

   b. As long as the ears are not injured seriously, hearing may recover naturally.

   c. There are various ways of cutting down on noise to protect our health.

   d. Mufflers are important devices which cause cars to sound louder than usual.

   e. As sound waves rebound off ceilings or walls, they become one of the causes of noise in a room.

   f. Putting rubber pads under machines is not an effective way of decreasing noise.

   g. Building an expensive house with soundproofing material is one way to block noise.

Lesson 7 比較

Grammar 目標➡ 7分

1 次の各組の文がほぼ同じ意味になるように、( )内に適語を補いなさい。 （各3点）

1. He was the greatest musician that ever lived in France.
   He was ( ) great a musician as ever lived in France.
2. Happiness consists in contentment rather than in wealth.
   Happiness consists not ( ) much in wealth as in contentment.
3. I can't cook. I can't even boil an egg.
   I can't cook. I can't so ( ) as boil an egg.
4. Bill is not such a fool as to argue with his boss.
   Bill knows ( ) than to argue with his boss.

2 次の各文の( )内に入れるのに最も適当なものを選び、記号を補いなさい。 （各2点）

1. The cost of the air fare is higher than ( ) of the rail fare.
   a. one　　　　　b. ones　　　　　c. that　　　　　d. those
2. I cannot use a computer ( ) more than a baby can.
   a. any　　　　　b. even　　　　　c. no　　　　　d. not
3. His house is no ( ) than a log cabin.
   a. better　　　　b. less　　　　　c. longer　　　　d. more
4. I prefer this coat ( ) the coat you were wearing yesterday.
   a. against　　　　b. for　　　　　c. than　　　　　d. to
5. Have you read Steinway's ( ) novel? It's much better than his last one.
   a. late　　　　　b. later　　　　　c. latter　　　　d. latest

Writing 目標➡ 3分

3 1.、2. は( )内の語句を並べかえなさい。3.、4. は英訳しなさい。

（1、2：各4点／3、4：各5点）

1. 海は、世界を分割しているというよりも、むしろ結びつけているのだ。
   Oceans don't so much (as / divide / it / the world / unite).

   _____

2. チンパンジーは、知的な面においては他のほとんどの動物たちよりも優れていると考えられている。
   Chimpanzees are considered (in / most / other animals / superior / to) intelligence.

   _____

3. ご返事をできるだけ早くお知らせください。
   Please let me know _____.

4. 私はこの雨の中を出かけるほど愚かではありません。

   _____

CAN-DO List □ 🔍 〈知識・技能〉比較を用いた表現、注意すべき比較表現を適切に活用できる。

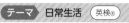
4 対話と質問を聞き、その答えとして最も適当なものを一つずつ選びなさい。 (各5点)

1. ① Give up shaving.
   ② Have his shaver fixed.
   ③ Go to a drugstore.
   ④ Shave in another way.

2. ① Two.
   ② Three.
   ③ Four.
   ④ Five.

Rapid Reading 目標➡5分 テーマ 商業

5 英文を読んで、次の問いに答えなさい。 (各5点)

Many people believe that advertising does not affect them. They feel that they have freedom of choice, and they like to think they make wise choices. Unfortunately, they probably don't realize the powerful effect of advertising. They may not clearly understand that advertisers spend billions of dollars each year in strong competition for our money, and they are extremely successful. Do you believe that ads don't influence your choice of products? Just look at the brands in your kitchen and bathroom.

1. What do most people feel that they have?
   ① Freedom of choosing products.
   ② A powerful effect on advertising.
   ③ Billions of dollars.
   ④ Brand-name products.

2. Which statement best expresses the main idea of the passage?
   ① Competition among advertisers helps people get better products.
   ② Most people are influenced by advertising without realizing it.
   ③ People should be wise enough to judge which brand is the best.
   ④ There are a few advertisers who try to control consumers' minds.

Reading　目標➡20分　　文法項目 注意すべき比較表現　テーマ 商業　　🔊 19

速読問題 次の英文を2.5分で読んで、1. の問いに答えなさい。

When I awoke the next morning, I felt a tiny but distinct thrill of (1)pleasurable anticipation. The routine of getting myself ready to face the world was, I knew, to be broken this morning. Then I remembered that having left my razor behind somewhere, the day before, I had bought a new and original safety razor and had been given with it a tube of new and entirely original

5　shaving cream.

Luxuriously I rose to play with these toys, but before using them I carefully read the makers' accounts of them on the outer wrappings.　The razor, I learned, was destined to revolutionize the practice of shaving; it was designed on a new principle; and (2)having given it the most superficial trial, I would never want to use any other.　The shaving cream was also

10　based on a new principle; it made shaving a pleasure; its *lather was so quick, so *foaming and creamy, so *soothing, that (3)you would be tempted to use this cream even without the excuse of needing a shave.　Inspired by these *rhapsodies, I began shaving at the earliest possible moment.

The cream was *wretched stuff; (4)the lather it made was no better than that from ordinary

15　soap; there was no sound reason for its existence.　The razor did not give me a proper shave at all; it was not that I could not handle it well, but simply that it could not cut hair.　I spent a good ten minutes scraping away with it, and even then I was only half shaved.

I am still wondering what the lying manufacturers of these articles had in their minds when they made them.　Were they merely depending upon a number of people, like me, to allow

20　ourselves to be fooled once?　Or did they honestly believe that they had turned out a good shaving cream and a good razor?　And if so, why?　They must have had plenty of opportunities to test the articles for themselves.　On the other hand, (5)surely it was hardly worth while going to the trouble and expense of manufacturing, advertising and marketing things they did not believe in themselves.

(357 words / 山梨大学)

---

10 lather[lǽðər]：泡　　10 foaming[fóumɪŋ]：泡立つ　　11 soothing[súːðɪŋ]：気持ちを落ち着かせる
12 rhapsody[rǽpsədi]：熱狂的な文章　　14 wretched[rétʃɪd]：みじめな、ひどい

CAN-DO List
□ 〈知識・技能〉比較を用いた表現、注意すべき比較表現を理解できる。
□ 〈思考力・判断力・表現力〉新しいカミソリとひげそりクリームの性能について的確に理解できる。

1. この英文は全体として何について述べていますか。次の a.～d. から選びなさい。　　（5点）

    a．朝の日課を一変させたかみそりとひげそりクリーム

    b．新製品が市場に登場するまでの生産者の試行錯誤

    c．新製品が消費者に受け入れられる要因

    d．まったくの期待はずれだったかみそりとひげそりクリーム

精 読問題 もう一度英文を読んで、次の問いに答えなさい。

2. 下線部(1)の「予感」の内容として最も適当なものを a.～d. から一つ選びなさい。　　（4点）

    a．また新しい一日が始まるのだということ。

    b．いつもとは違う朝になるのだろうということ。

    c．使いにくいかみそりを使わなければならないこと。

    d．かみそりをどこかに置き忘れたこと。

3. 下線部(2)、(3)の意味を、わかりやすく日本語で説明しなさい。　　（各6点）

    (2) _____

    (3) _____

4. **文法** 下線部(4)を和訳しなさい。　　（6点）

_____

5. 下線部(5)を和訳しなさい。　　（6点）

_____

6. **全体把握** 本文の内容と合っているものにはＴ、合っていないものにはＦと答えなさい。　（各1点）

(ア) The day before, the author bought a new razor and new shaving cream.　　(　　　)

(イ) According to the maker, the razor would change the practice of shaving completely.

(　　　)

(ウ) After reading the makers' accounts, the author began shaving as soon as possible.

(　　　)

(エ) The lather from the cream was just like what ordinary soap makes.　　(　　　)

(オ) It took the author ten minutes to have a clean shave with the razor.　　(　　　)

(カ) Surely the makers honestly believe that they have produced a good shaving cream and a good razor.　　(　　　)

(キ) Surely the makers themselves do not believe in the shaving cream or the razor.

(　　　)

Lesson 8 関係詞

Grammar　目標➡ 7分

1 次の各文の（　　）内に入れるのに最も適当なものを選び、記号を補いなさい。　　　　（各2点）

1. What's the name of the hotel (　　　)?
   - a. you stayed at
   - b. you stayed with
   - c. where you stayed in
   - d. which you stayed

2. Hawaii is a place (　　　) attracts visitors from all over the world.
   - a. as
   - b. where
   - c. what
   - d. which

3. Last night Cindy told me about her new job in Tokyo, (　　　) she appears to be enjoying very much.
   - a. which
   - b. where
   - c. what
   - d. when

4. You may invite (　　　) wants to come.
   - a. whomever
   - b. whoever
   - c. who
   - d. anyone

5. (　　　) I try, I'll never beat her at tennis.
   - a. However hard
   - b. How strongly
   - c. In which way
   - d. What way

6. No matter what (　　　), some people complain about it.
   - a. is the weather like
   - b. the weather is like
   - c. like is the weather
   - d. is like the weather

7. Everybody agrees that the United States today is a very different country from (　　　) it was thirty years ago.
   - a. when
   - b. what
   - c. where
   - d. how

8. It is often said that rice is to Asians (　　　) wheat is to Europeans.
   - a. how
   - b. that
   - c. what
   - d. which

Writing　目標➡ 3分

2 （　　）内の語句を並べかえて英文を完成しなさい。　　　　（各5点）

1. 私の住んでいる通りは夜騒がしくて、なかなか眠れません。
   The street I live on is noisy at night, (difficult / it / makes / sleep / to / which).

   _____

2. たとえどんなに狭くても、私は自分の部屋をもちたいのです。
   I'd rather have a room of my own, (how / is / it / matter / no / small).

   _____

3. 小論文には、書きたいと思うどんなテーマでも選んでよろしい。
   You can choose (to / topic / want / whatever / write about / you) for your essay.

   _____

　CAN-DO List　□ 🔍　〈知識・技能〉いろいろな関係詞の働きを理解し、適切に活用できる。

3 長めの対話を一つ聞き、問いの答えとして最も適当なものを一つずつ選びなさい。対話の前に Situation が読み上げられます。 (各5点)

Situation：A man and a woman are having a conversation on a long-distance train.

1. How long has the woman lived in Seattle?
   ① Since last year.
   ② For a few days.
   ③ Since several years ago.
   ④ Since she was born.

2. What is the man going to do in Spokane?
   ① Attend an event held there.
   ② Meet his client there.
   ③ Drive to the countryside.
   ④ Go back home to see his family.

Rapid Reading 目標➡5分 テーマ 故郷 英検®

4 （1）・（2）に入れるのに最も適当なものを一つずつ選びなさい。 (各5点)

　An English village is usually a very attractive place.　It consists of a small group of houses surrounded by green fields, bushes, and trees.　All the houses and cottages have （　1　）, in which flowers bloom from spring to autumn.　There is always a church, with a graveyard next to it, a *public house, and a general store.　Sometimes a stream flows past the houses.　Often there is only one street, and it is kept clean and tidy.　The inhabitants are proud of their village and do their best （　2　）.

> ⁴ public house：居酒屋

1. ① farmland ② gardens
   ③ barns ④ parks
2. ① to protect its plants
   ② to develop it into a modern city
   ③ to make it look attractive
   ④ to make it unknown to the outer world

速読問題 次の英文を2.5分で読んで、1. の問いに答えなさい。

One thing that is important to very many English people is where they are from. (1)For many of us, whatever happens to us in later life, and however much we move house or travel, the place where we grew up and spent our childhood and *adolescence retains a special significance. Of course, this is not true of all of us. More often than in previous generations,

5 families may move around the country, and there are increasing numbers of people who have had a *nomadic childhood and are not really "from" anywhere. (2)But for a majority of English people, pride and interest in the area where they grew up is still a reality. The country is full of football supporters whose main concern is for the club of their childhood, even though they may now live hundreds of miles away. Local newspapers *crisscross the country in their

10 thousands on their way to "*exiles" who have left their local areas. And at Christmas time the roads and railways are full of people returning to their *native heath for the holiday period.

Where we are from is thus an important part of our personal identity, and for many of us an important component of this local identity is the way we speak —— our accent and *dialect. (3)Nearly all of us have regional features in the way we speak English, and are happy

15 that this is so, although of course there are upper-class people who have regionless accents, as well as people who, for some reason, wish to conceal their regional origins. The vast majority of the population, however, speak in a manner which identifies them as coming from a particular place. They speak like the people they grew up with, and in a way that is different from people who grew up somewhere else. Of course, people may change the way in which

20 they speak during their lifetimes, especially if they move around the country, but most of us (4)carry at least some trace of our accent and dialect origins with us all of our lives.

(343 words / 滋賀大学)

---

³ adolescence [ædəlés(ə)ns]：青年期、思春期　　⁶ nomadic [noʊmǽdɪk]：遊牧民的な、頻繁に転居する
⁹ crisscross [krískrɔ̀ːs]：…を縦横に動く、…の中を行き来する　　¹⁰ exile [éksaɪl]：亡命者
¹¹ native heath：生まれ（育った）故郷　　¹⁴ dialect [dá(ɪ)əlèkt]：方言

CAN-DO List　□ 〈知識・技能〉いろいろな関係詞の働きについて理解できる。
　　　　　　　□ 〈思考力・判断力・表現力〉故郷と地元言葉への思いについて的確に理解できる。

1. この英文は全体として何について述べていますか。次の a.～d.から選びなさい。　　（5点）

   a．故郷を失ってしまった現代のイングランド人

   b．故郷や地方なまりに対して抱くイングランド人の複雑な思い

   c．自分の故郷と地方なまりを大切にするイングランド人

   d．どうしても消せないイングランド人の地方なまり

精 読問題 もう一度英文を読んで、次の問いに答えなさい。

2. 文法 下線部(1)を和訳しなさい。　　（5点）

_____

3. 下線部(2)を具体的に表している現象を、日本語で三つ挙げなさい。　　（各5点）

_____

_____

4. 下線部(3)について、Nearly all of us に含まれない人々にはどんな人々がいますか。日本語で二つ挙げなさい。　　（各5点）

_____

_____

5. 下線部(3)について、have regional features in the way we speak English をわかりやすい日本語で説明しなさい。　　（6点）

_____

6. 下線部(4)の carry とほぼ同じ意味の carry を含む文を a.～d.から一つ選びなさい。　　（4点）

   a．A train carrying hundreds of passengers crashed yesterday.

   b．The telephone can carry your voice anywhere in the world.

   c．These pillars cannot carry the whole weight of the roof.

   d．John has carried the habit of twiddling his thumbs from his childhood.

7. 全体把握 次の英文の ア ～ イ に入れるのに最も適当なものを、下の a.～d.のうちから一つずつ選びなさい。ただし、文頭にくるべき語も小文字で示しています。　　（各2点）

   ア means a lot to many English people because it is an important part of their personal identity.　They are also proud of イ because it identifies them as coming from a particular place.

   a．the people they grew up with

   b．the place where they grew up

   c．the way they speak English

   d．what is different from others

   ア（　　　）　イ（　　　）

Lesson 9 仮定法

Grammar　目標➡ 7分

1 次の各文の（　　）内に入れるのに最も適当なものを選び、記号を補いなさい。　　（各2点）

1. If I (　　　) a computer last year, I'd still be using my old typewriter.
   a. hadn't bought　　b. haven't bought　　c. shouldn't buy　　d. wouldn't buy

2. If you had had some breakfast, you (　　　) hungry now.
   a. are not　　　　　　　　　　　b. were not
   c. would not be　　　　　　　　d. would not have been

3. It's after ten o'clock, Jack!　It's about time you (　　　) to bed.
   a. will go　　　b. had been　　　c. have gone　　　d. went

4. (　　　) the greenhouse effect, the climate on the earth would be much colder.
   a. Without　　　b. Unless　　　c. At　　　d. To

5. He just failed the examination——two more points and he (　　　).
   a. would have passed　　　　　　b. would pass
   c. would not have passed　　　　d. would not pass

6. She ran;(　　　), she would have missed her bus.
   a. however　　　b. moreover　　　c. otherwise　　　d. therefore

7. Jim had a skiing accident yesterday, but he was all right.　He was lucky, because he (　　　) hurt himself badly.
   a. could have　　　b. might　　　c. should　　　d. will have

Writing　目標➡ 3分

2 1.～3. は（　　）内の語句を並べかえなさい。4.、5. は英訳しなさい。

(1～3：各3点／4、5：各5点)

1. もし私たちが地図を持って来ていたら、どちらの道を行けばいいかわかるのにね。
   If we (a map / brought / had / us / with), we would know which road to take.

   _____

2. 私の立場だったらあなたはどうしますか。
   What (do / if / in / my position / were / would / you / you)?

   _____

3. 思いやりのある人ならだれでも、おばあさんが道を渡る手助けをします。
   Any considerate person (an old lady / assistance / give / in / would) crossing the street.

   _____

4. もう散髪をしてもらってもいいころですよ。

   _____

5. 試験というものがなかったら、私たちはもっと幸せなのだが。

   _____

　CAN-DO List　□ 🔍　〈知識・技能〉いろいろな仮定法を適切に活用できる。

3 それぞれの写真について4つの説明が読まれます。写真に最も合っているものを一つずつ選びなさい。 (各5点)

1.

① ② ③ ④

2.

① ② ③ ④

Rapid Reading 目標➡5分 テーマ 自然 英検®

4 (1)・(2)に入れるのに最も適当なものを一つずつ選びなさい。 (各5点)

The redwood trees of Northern California are among the tallest and oldest trees on Earth. Because a single tree can live to be more than 2,000 years old, there are some redwoods alive today that were already tall trees (1). They are also very wide at the bottom. One tree has a large hole in the bottom. (2) that you can drive a car through it.

1. ① 2,000 years ago
   ② when Native Americans planted the forest
   ③ when Columbus arrived in America in 1492
   ④ when they were cut down for heating or building
2. ① The bottom is so wide
   ② The hole is so big
   ③ The tree is so tall
   ④ The tree is so old

Reading 目標➡20分　文法項目 いろいろな仮定法　テーマ 自然　◆)) 24

速読問題 次の英文を2.5分で読んで、1. の問いに答えなさい。

Whenever you think of the Wild West, you think of cowboy movies with tumbleweed rolling about in the wind.　According to these movies, tumbleweed is as American as apple pie.　Tumbleweed, however, is not native to North America.　(1)It is said to have arrived in the United States in shipments of *flax seeds from Russia to South Dakota in the nineteenth
5　century.　Within twenty years the tumbleweed spread to more than a dozen states.

The tumbleweed is a rather peculiar plant, because it does not spend its whole life in the soil.　Once its seeds are ripe, it breaks off at the base of its stem.　At this stage it is almost a perfect ball, with about 250,000 seeds stored inside.　The wind then takes control of the tumbleweed.　(2)The plant is designed so that when the ball hits the ground, it bounces, and
10　won't lose all of its valuable seeds in just a single bounce.

(3)Tumbleweed drove many farmers from their homes.　It was so frightening, but nothing could stop it.　The wind rolled this plant around.　Being very dry and light, the tumbleweed easily caught fire, and set fire to crops and houses.　It also had very sharp pointy leaves that penetrated heavy leather gloves and cut horses' legs.　Overall, the tumbleweed was an
15　environmental disaster.

The real reason tumbleweed *thrived was agriculture.　In the American Midwest, the tall prairie grasses would have made it impossible for the tumbleweed to roll any distance, but the grasses had been replaced by *plowed fields.　The tumbleweed followed the farmers and spread very rapidly.　(4)Without agriculture, it would have been a minor plant, growing in
20　desert areas.

The tumbleweed, however, (5)has a lot going for it.　In dry regions, it is used as food for farm animals.　It is also said to improve the soil by *trickling chemicals into the soil.　These chemicals make the nutrients in the soil more available to other plants.　Once tumbleweed has grown in the soil, other plants grow better the next season.　But best of all, it is a survivor.
25　In southern Nevada, where many nuclear weapons were tested above ground, the tumbleweed was always the first plant to start growing at *ground zero.　　　　(369 words / 大阪学院大学)

CAN-DO List　☐ ◉ 〈知識・技能〉いろいろな仮定法について理解できる。
☐ ● 〈思考力・判断力・表現力〉タンブルウィードという植物について的確に理解できる。

⁴flax seed：亜麻の種子　　¹⁶thrive[θráɪv]：生い茂る　　¹⁸plow[pláʊ]：…を耕す
²²trickle[trík(ə)l]：…を流し込む　　²⁶ground zero：ゼロ地点（原水爆の爆心地）

1. この英文は全体として何について述べていますか。次のa.〜d.から選びなさい。　　　　　　（5点）
　　a. 合衆国の農業の発達に貢献したタンブルウィード
　　b. タンブルウィードが合衆国全土に広がった理由
　　c. タンブルウィードとはどんな植物か
　　d. タンブルウィードの有益性と有害性

精 読問題　もう一度英文を読んで、次の問いに答えなさい。

2. 下線部(1)を、Itの具体的な内容を明らかにして、和訳しなさい。　　　　　　　　　　　　（8点）

_____

3. 下線部(2)を和訳しなさい。　　　　　　　　　　　　　　　　　　　　　　　　　　　（7点）

_____

4. 下線部(3)の理由を、具体的に日本語で説明しなさい。　　　　　　　　　　　　　　　　　（8点）

_____

5. 文法 下線部(4)の理由を、日本語で説明しなさい。　　　　　　　　　　　　　　　　　　（8点）

_____

6. 下線部(5)の意味として最も適当なものをa.〜d.から一つ選びなさい。　　　　　　　　　　（3点）
　　a. 今なお、はびこっている　　　　　　　　　b. 嫌われる要因を多くもつ
　　c. 今後広がっていく土地を多くもつ　　　　　d. 支持される要因を多くもつ

7. 全体把握 本文の内容と合っているものにはT、合っていないものにはFと答えなさい。（各1点）
　(ア) タンブルウィードの種子は、他の種子に混じって、19世紀にロシアから入って来たと言われている。　　　　　　　　　　　　　　　　　　　　　　　　　　　　　　　　　　　（　　　）
　(イ) 花が満開になると、タンブルウィードは根元近くの茎のところで折れる。　　　　（　　　）
　(ウ) タンブルウィードは球状で軽く、転がりながら種子を落としていく。　　　　　　（　　　）
　(エ) タンブルウィードの種子は、風に乗ってあっという間に全米に広がった。　　　　（　　　）
　(オ) 軽く、乾燥しているタンブルウィードには火がつきやすく、火災の原因となった。（　　　）
　(カ) タンブルウィードの鋭いとげで、人や馬が大けがをするので嫌われていた。　　　（　　　）
　(キ) 中西部の草原地帯が開墾されると、タンブルウィードは砂漠地帯へと広まっていった。
　　　　　　　　　　　　　　　　　　　　　　　　　　　　　　　　　　　　　　　（　　　）
　(ク) タンブルウィードは生命力が旺盛で、核実験地でも常に最初に再生した。　　　　（　　　）

Lesson 10 名詞・代名詞

Grammar 目標➡7分

1 次の各文の（　　）内に入れるのに最も適当なものを選び、記号を補いなさい。　（各2点）

1. I need (　　　) about hotels in Mexico City.
   - a. an information
   - b. informations
   - c. some information
   - d. some informations

2. Unemployment compensation is money to support an unemployed person while he or she is looking for (　　　).
   - a. job
   - b. a job
   - c. works
   - d. a work

3. Mr. and Mrs. Smith have bought (　　　) for their living room.
   - a. a modern furniture
   - b. modern furnitures
   - c. some modern furniture
   - d. some modern furnitures

4. We had (　　　) when we were on vacation.
   - a. a wonderful weather
   - b. wonderful weathers
   - c. wonderful weather
   - d. some wonderful weathers

5. Fortunately, the news (　　　) as bad as we expected.
   - a. was
   - b. wasn't
   - c. were
   - d. weren't

6. The police (　　　) to interview two men about the robbery last week.
   - a. are wanting
   - b. is wanting
   - c. want
   - d. wants

7. To learn is one thing, and to teach is (　　　).
   - a. the other
   - b. the one
   - c. other
   - d. another

8. The runners came back to the stadium one (　　　) another.
   - a. by
   - b. after
   - c. through
   - d. from

Writing 目標➡3分

2 1.～3. は（　　）内の語句を並べかえなさい。4.、5. は英訳しなさい。

（1～3：各4点／4、5：各5点）

1. This old French table is (a / furniture / piece / of / valuable / very).
   _____

2. Can you give me (about / advice / course / some / which) to take?
   _____

3. You should try to be (more sensitive / of / others / the needs / to).
   _____

4. ジョージは失業中です。職を探しています。
   George is unemployed. _____

5. もう一杯コーヒーはいかがですか。
   _____

Listening

目標→5分 テーマ 空港 共通テスト 25

3 英語を聞き、4つの空欄 [1]～[4] に入れるのに最も適当なものを4つの選択肢①～④から一つずつ選びなさい。 (各2点)

Number of International Passengers by Airport

Others 4%
Narita 34%
[1] 3%
New Chitose 4%
[2] 6%
Chubu Centrair 7%
[3] 18%
[4] 24%

① Kansai
② Haneda
③ Fukuoka
④ Naha

1 (　)
2 (　)
3 (　)
4 (　)

Rapid Reading

目標→5分 テーマ ジェンダー平等 共通テスト

4 SNSを読み取って、問いに対する答えとして最も適当なものを一つずつ選びなさい。 (各5点)

How Can We Contribute to Gender Equality?

Post by Brian Williams

Gender equality should not be seen just as a women's issue. It is also an issue that requires men and women to work together in order to find a solution. One great speech has made me realize this. In 2014, as a Goodwill Ambassador for the United Nations, Emma Watson, who is a British actress and model, gave a smart, moving speech about gender inequality and how to fight it. Not only women but also men should be aware of what we can do to achieve gender equality. In her speech, she said, "We are struggling for a united world but the good news is we have a uniting movement. It is called HeForShe." This speech has made me realize the importance of our responsibility.

Comments
From Daniel Grint

In her speech, she used the phrase, "If not me, who? If not now, when?" several times. Emma does not need her question to be answered. Instead, by asking such a kind of question, she is trying to say that each of us is responsible for gender equality. Being aware of the issue of gender equality is the very first step in finding its solution. I believe she used a magic spell in her speech!

1. Brian has realized the importance of gender equality from the fact that "[　]"
   ① Emma Watson gave an impressive speech in 2014.
   ② Gender equality is an issue that we should understand well.
   ③ Emma Watson is struggling to unite the world.
   ④ Gender equality is becoming a new movement called HeForShe.

2. Why did Emma Watson use the phrase, "If not me, who? If not now, when?"
   ① She wanted everyone to be aware of the responsibility for gender equality.
   ② She wanted to get a good solution from other people.
   ③ She thought she could use a magic spell to persuade people.
   ④ She thought she was responsible for spreading the idea of gender equality.

CAN-DO List 〈思考力・判断力・表現力〉英文を聞いて、グラフを正しく読み取ることができる。 〈思考力・判断力・表現力〉SNSの投稿から、男女平等の意見について読み取ることができる。 **Lesson 10** 41

速 読問題 次の英文を2.5分で読んで、1. の問いに答えなさい。

More men are taking jobs as flight attendants in the traditionally female-dominated profession as smaller Japanese airlines actively try to distinguish themselves from their larger domestic rivals.　The increasingly physical (1)nature of the work, combined with the growing need to deal with unruly or drunk passengers, means (2)so-called *soradan* are being seen in the

5 skies above Japan in larger numbers.　The change also demonstrates how the domestic airline industry is slowly modernizing and gender roles are beginning to reflect what is considered normal across much of the world.

Koichi Ito, 38, joined Star Flyer, a midsize carrier, as a flight attendant after a period working at a hotel.　Ito said that, as a student, he was impressed by the male flight attendants he would

10 see aboard foreign carriers.　(3)Some possible advantages of being a male attendant include helping passengers load and unload their increasingly large *carry-on luggage and other more physical tasks, Ito noted.　"Male and female flight attendants have a different sense for passenger needs, and by combining both genders, the quality of service improves," he said.

Star Flyer has eight men among its 160 flight attendants and plans to hire six more male

15 attendants by next summer.　"The use of male flight attendants is effective in impressing upon passengers that we offer a different service from big airlines," said a Star Flyer *public relations official.

(4)Foreign airlines employ many men as flight attendants, reflecting a difference between their concept of *hospitality and that of domestic airlines.　Men are only about 1 percent of

20 the flight attendants at both of the country's two major airlines—Japan Airlines and All Nippon Airways—considerably lower than the 40 percent at Singapore Airlines and the 10 percent at Korean Air Lines.

Japanese airlines had until recently almost exclusively employed young female attendants on international flights, apparently to please their business clients who are mostly men,

25 according to an executive of a leading domestic airline.

(5)But now the situation is changing.　"An increase in young women and foreigners among passengers has created various needs, including those that can be better met by male crew members," said Hiroki Nakamura, 38, a male attendant with Japan Airlines.　"We've also seen a rise in male flight attendants in their 20s," he said.　*Aviation analyst Kotaro Toriumi said an

30 increase in the number of female flight attendants who continue to work in the field after marriage

CAN-DO List　☐ 〈知識・技能〉用法を誤りやすい名詞と代名詞について理解できる。
☐ 〈思考力・判断力・表現力〉男性客室乗務員の増加について的確に理解できる。

and childbirth has changed the perception about the occupation, with men now considering it a

practical career choice and, it seems, valuing it more highly. (426 words / 神戸学院大学)

The Japan Times (2019年1月4日掲載 *The Japan Times Alpha*)

¹¹carry-on luggage：機内持ち込み手荷物　　¹⁶public relations：広報
¹⁹hospitality［hɑ̀(ː)spətǽləti］：もてなし　　²⁹aviation［èɪviéɪʃ(ə)n］：航空

1．この英文のタイトルとして最も適当なものを、次のa.～d.から選びなさい。　　　　（5点）
　　a．More Men Joining Cabin Crews as Flight Attendants in Japan
　　b．More Jobs for Women Taken Away by Men in Japan
　　c．More Flight Attendants Demanding Various Needs and Opportunities
　　d．More Young Women and Men Choosing Flight Attendants as Their Jobs

精 読問題 もう一度英文を読んで、次の問いに答えなさい。

2．文法 下線部(1)の nature と同じ意味を持つものを a.～d.から一つ選びなさい。　　（5点）
　　a．Scientists studied and discovered the nature of the universe.
　　b．Galileo tested hypotheses about the laws of nature with experiments.
　　c．People by nature are curious about the world around them.
　　d．The Thai government has created a new nature reserve.

3．下線部(2)のように *soradan* と呼ばれる客室乗務員が増えた理由を、日本語で説明しなさい。　　（5点）

4．下線部(3)の「長所」について次の日本文の（　　）内に適語を入れ、具体的な内容を答えなさい。（各3点）
　（①　　　　　　　　　　　）機内持ち込み手荷物の（②　　　　　　　　　　）、そして、その他の体力を使う作業の
　手伝いができること。

5．下線部(4)について、国内外の航空会社の男性客室乗務員の割合についてまとめた表を完成しなさい。
（各2点）

Airline Company	The percentage of male flight attendants
① [　　　　　　　]	1 %
All Nippon Airways	② [　　　　　]
Star Flyer	③ [　　　　　]
④ [　　　　　　　]	40%
Korean Air Lines	⑤ [　　　　　]

6．下線部(5)のように状況が変化してきている理由を、50字から60字程度の日本語で答えなさい。　　（5点）

7．全体把握 本文の内容と合うように、（　　）内に適当な一語を補いなさい。　　（完答各2点）
　① Today, more (　　　　　　　) are choosing to be flight attendants as their job, although it has
　　 been traditionally seen as a (　　　　　　) job.
　② Koichi Ito is now working for Star Flyer as a (　　　　　　) (　　　　　　) after having
　　 worked at a (　　　　　).
　③ Star Flyer is planning to hire six more (　　　　　　) attendants by next (　　　　　　).
　④ According to Kotaro Toriumi, more (　　　　　) flight attendants are (　　　　　) to
　　 work after (　　　　　) and childbirth.

Lesson **11** 副詞

1 次の各文の（　　）内に下記の語群から適語を選んで補いなさい。　　　　（各2点）

1. (　　　　　　　　), it stopped raining before the picnic started.
2. (　　　　　　　　), I would like to go to bed; I'm tired.
3. (　　　　　　　　), the ambulance was held up by heavy traffic.
4. (　　　　　　　) enough, he can't speak a word of French though he has lived in France for years.
5. (　　　　　　　　), you should apologize for being rude.

【Fortunately / Naturally / Obviously / Strangely / Unfortunately】

2 次の各文の（　　）内に入れるのに最も適当なものを選び、記号を補いなさい。　　（各2点）

1. Some of the food crops failed. (　　　　), the cotton did quite well.
   - a. However　　　　　b. In addition　　　　c. Moreover　　　　d. First of all
2. It's raining. (　　　), the picnic is canceled.
   - a. However　　　　　b. Or else　　　　　　c. Otherwise　　　　d. Therefore
3. Mary didn't want to go out for a walk.　The weather was wet and miserable. (　　　　), she had a headache.
   - a. Besides　　　　　b. However　　　　　c. Otherwise　　　　d. Therefore
4. I would wear an overcoat if I were you; (　　　), you'll catch a cold.
   - a. however　　　　　b. moreover　　　　　c. otherwise　　　　d. therefore

3 1.～3. は（　　）内の語句を並べかえなさい。4.、5. は英訳しなさい。

(1～3：各3点／4、5：各5点)

1. Fortunately, the fire (after / had started / it / soon / was discovered).

   _____

2. Surprisingly enough, some foreign actors are (in / in / Japan / more / popular / than / their own countries).

   _____

3. A driver of a car must wear a seat belt.　Similarly, (all / in / must also / the car / the passengers) wear seat belts.

   _____

4. 彼の歌は十代の若者の間では人気があった。しかし、大人たちは彼の歌を好まなかった。
   His songs were popular among teenagers.　_____
5. このシャツの色が好きではないし、それに値段が高すぎます。

   _____

4 長めの対話を一つ聞き、問いの答えとして最も適当なものを一つずつ選びなさい。 （各5点）

1. Why is the woman going to take German?
   ① Because she thinks it will be of use.
   ② Because her friends advised her to take it.
   ③ To perform classical music in the future.
   ④ Because she doesn't know how difficult it is.

2. What does the man think of French?
   ① It has a lot of verb forms.
   ② Pronouncing it is difficult.
   ③ Its grammar is more complex.
   ④ It is not as difficult as German.

Rapid Reading 目標➡5分 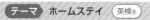 テーマ ホームステイ 英検®

5 （1）・（2）に入れるのに最も適当なものを一つずつ選びなさい。 （各5点）

I had an interesting experience with my host family in New Zealand.　I began talking about Ichiro, the Japanese baseball star, but their faces (　1　).　I couldn't believe it.　They didn't know who he was.　So I said, "Ichiro's a very famous baseball player not only in Japan, but also in the United States.　He's on TV all the time.　Everyone knows him!"　That's when I first realized that (　2　).

1. ① clouded over
   ② lighted up
   ③ turned pale
   ④ went blank
2. ① common knowledge differs from country to country
   ② Japanese names were easy to remember
   ③ my English did not make any sense
   ④ people in New Zealand are very interested in Japan

速読問題 次の英文を2.5分で読んで、1. の問いに答えなさい。

I have a baby granddaughter, who lives far away from me (in *Perth) but whom I often visit. When I come back from (1)these visits (to *Canberra), and when my *Anglophone friends ask me how she is, (2)I am often stuck for words. I just can't find English words suitable for talking about my tiny granddaughter. It is not that I am unfamiliar with

5 the (3)register of English used for talking about babies, but I feel that this register does not fit the emotional world to which this baby belongs for me. No doubt one reason is that Polish was my first language and that as such it is endowed with an emotional force that English doesn't have for me. But this is not the only reason. Another reason is that Polish words which I could use to talk about my baby granddaughter do not have exact *semantic

10 equivalents in English and therefore (4)feel *irreplaceable. For example, I could say in Polish that she is *rozkoszna*, using a word rendered in Polish-English dictionaries as 'delightful,' but I couldn't possibly use the word 'delightful' about her myself——not only because it has no emotional force for me but because its meaning, which is not identical with that of *rozkoszna*, doesn't fit my way of thinking and feeling about this baby. *Rozkoszna* has a greater emotional

15 force *by virtue of its meaning, and 'delightful' would sound, from the point of view of a bilingual but culturally *predominantly Polish person, too light, too objective and too lacking in emotional intensity.

In fact, in English, too, most people would probably be reluctant to describe their own child or grandchild as 'delightful,' because the word appears to imply an outsider's perspective and

20 a lack of personal emotional involvement. They might, however, describe their own child or grandchild as 'adorable,' or as 'a cutie,' or 'a sweetie' or 'a dear little thing'; and they might describe other people's babies as 'gorgeous.' None of (5)these options are available to me. I feel I couldn't use any of these expressions about my little granddaughter, not only because they all leave me cold but because their meaning does not fit my own way of thinking and

25 feeling, and so (6)they would not sound 'true' to me. (377 words / 兵庫県立大学)

---

¹Perth[pə́ːrθ]：パース(オーストラリア西海岸の都市)
²Canberra[kǽnb(ə)rə]：キャンベラ(オーストラリアの首都) ²Anglophone[ǽŋgləfòʊn]：英語を話す
⁹semantic[səmǽntɪk]：意味に関する ¹⁰irreplaceable[ìrɪpléɪsəb(ə)l]：代用できない
¹⁵by virtue of ...：…の力のおかげで ¹⁶predominantly[prɪdɑ́(ː)mɪnəntli]：主に、圧倒的に

CAN-DO List □ 〈知識・技能〉文修飾副詞、2つの文のつながりを示す副詞について理解できる。
□ 〈思考力・判断力・表現力〉他言語では表現しきれない母語の表現の話について理解できる。

1. この英文の筆者の説明として最も適当なものを、次のa.～d.から選びなさい。　　　（5点）
   a. 英語の感情表現の少なさに驚いているポーランド人
   b. オーストラリアに移住して、英語で苦労しているポーランド人
   c. 故郷のポーランドがどうしても忘れられない移住者
   d. 孫娘のかわいさを英語では表現できないと考えているポーランド人

精 読問題 もう一度英文を読んで、次の問いに答えなさい。

2. 下線部(1)の具体的な内容を、日本語で説明しなさい。　　　（5点）
_____

3. 下線部(2)の状況を、日本語で具体的に説明しなさい。　　　（6点）
_____

4. 下線部(3)と最も近い意味で用いられているものをa.～d.から一つ選びなさい。　　　（3点）
   a. All new guests must sign the hotel register.
   b. His essay suddenly switches from a formal to an informal register.
   c. She was working at the cash register at the front of the store.
   d. Can you speak in a lower register and a little slower?

5. 文法 下線部(4)の理由を、日本語で説明しなさい。　　　（6点）
_____

6. 下線部(5)の指すものを、英語で列挙しなさい。　　　（5点）
_____

7. 下線部(6)の理由を、日本語で説明しなさい。　　　（6点）
_____

8. 全体把握 本文の内容と合っているものにはT、合っていないものにはFと答えなさい。（各1点）
   (ア) The author doesn't know English words that she could use to talk about babies.
   （　　　）
   (イ) Polish was the author's native language, so it has an emotional force that English doesn't have for her.　　　（　　　）
   (ウ) The author feels there are a few English equivalents to the Polish "rozkoszna."
   （　　　）
   (エ) According to Polish-English dictionaries, "rozkoszna" is the word for "delightful."
   （　　　）
   (オ) The author can speak both Polish and English well, and lives in Australia, but she has Polish ways of living there.　　　（　　　）
   (カ) A pretty little child is sometimes called "a cutie."　　　（　　　）
   (キ) The author is not pleased or excited about talking about her little granddaughter in English.　　　（　　　）

Lesson 12 接続詞・前置詞

Grammar 目標➡7分

1 次の各文の（　　）内に入れるのに最も適当なものを選び、記号を補いなさい。　　　　(各2点)

1. The tides of the earth's oceans rise and fall (　　) the influence of the moon.
   a. as to
   b. in spite of
   c. in addition to
   d. owing to

2. Now, (　　) to high technology, we can travel very fast.
   a. true
   b. according
   c. thanks
   d. comparing

3. You will get paid (　　) to the number of hours that you work.
   a. addition
   b. according
   c. owing
   d. thanks

4. Most thoughts are expressed by (　　) of words.
   a. the way
   b. hand
   c. and large
   d. means

5. (　　) that we are eighteen, we must take care of ourselves.
   a. Once
   b. Now
   c. Thus
   d. When

6. He doesn't care how he dresses (　　) his clothes are clean.
   a. as if
   b. as well as
   c. as long as
   d. as far as

7. As (　　) as I can see, there is no easy solution to this problem.
   a. far
   b. long
   c. much
   d. well

8. (　　) the time the firefighters arrived, the fire had already been put out.
   a. At
   b. By
   c. In
   d. On

9. (　　) time you come, please let me know so we can meet.
   a. By
   b. The first
   c. The last
   d. The next

10. (　　) all the warnings, many people continue to smoke.
    a. Although
    b. Instead of
    c. In spite of
    d. In addition to

11. I wear my seat belt (　　) I have an accident.
    a. as long as
    b. even if
    c. in case
    d. unless

Writing 目標➡3分

2 1.、2. は（　　）内の語句を並べかえなさい。3.、4. は英訳しなさい。

(1、2：各4点／3、4：各5点)

1. Mary was (a / deep / in / sleep / such) that she did not hear her mother call.
   _____

2. Cigarette smoke can have harmful effects not just on the smoker, (but also / live / on / people / who / with the smoker).
   _____

3. 帽子をかぶったままで部屋に入って来るなともう何度も言ったはずだぞ。
   I've told you a hundred times not to _____ .

4. 子供たちは、食事を終えて川へ泳ぎに行きました。
   _____

CAN-DO List □ 〈知識・技能〉群前置詞、群接続詞を適切に活用できる。

3 英文と質問を聞き、その答えとして最も適当なものを一つずつ選びなさい。 （各5点）

1. ① To go on to the higher education.
　② To find employment in Japan.
　③ To learn language skills for academic purposes.
　④ To become good at Japanese.

2. ① In the same way as animals treat humans.
　② In the same way as humans are.
　③ Equally with other creatures on Earth.
　④ Differently from humans.

Rapid Reading 目標➡5分　テーマ 教育 英検®

4 メールを読み取って、問いに対する答えとして最も適当なものを一つずつ選びなさい。 （各5点）

From : Bill Evans　<b-evans7@heatmeal.com>
To : Naoko Ishibashi naoko.bridgestone@capitalstar.ac.jp
Date : March 7
Subject : The Earlier, the Better?
Hi, Naoko,

　Thank you for joining us last week.　The next topic is, "The earlier, the better for English learning at school?"　Some people in Japan believe that if you start learning English at an earlier age, you will become better at English more quickly.　They believe there is a critical period in early childhood. This theory is that a child can easily learn a language perfectly during the early years.

　Do you think this means that earlier is always better for English learning at school?　Not necessarily.　Successful bilingual children have been raised in an environment where they use the second language at all times.　Learning a second language in the classroom is an entirely different matter.　Most classrooms cannot give the thousands of hours necessary for language learning.

　In the next discussion session, please tell us your ideas about this topic.
Best,
Bill

---

1. What does Bill want Naoko to do?
　① To collect information from the people around her.
　② To learn how to teach English easily.
　③ To use the second language at any time.
　④ To think about the topic and talk about her idea.

2. Why can some children become a successful bilingual?
　① They can easily learn the second language without making much effort.
　② They may have been in an environment where they use the target language all the time.
　③ They are given the thousands of hours necessary for language learning.
　④ They have experienced a special language learning program at school.

速 読問題 次の英文を2.5分で読んで、1. の問いに答えなさい。

Standing before an audience that included her parents, Malala Yousafzai, the youngest person in history to receive a Nobel Prize, stated, "Let this be the last time that a girl gets forced into early child marriage.   Let this be the last time a child remains out of school.   (1)Let us begin this ending."

5　Born in Pakistan in 1997, Malala grew up in an area controlled by (2)the *Taliban, who often used violence to prevent girls from going to school.   When she was only eleven years old, she gave a speech titled "How dare the Taliban take away my basic right to education?"

Malala continued to speak out about her right, and the right of all women, to an education. When she was 14, Malala and her family learned that the Taliban had issued a death threat

10　against her.   Though Malala was concerned about the safety of her father, she and her family at first felt that the terrorist group would not actually harm a child.   However, on October 9, 2012, on her way home from school, a man boarded the bus Malala was riding in and demanded to know which girl was Malala.   When her friends looked toward Malala, (3)her location was given away.   The man fired at her, hitting Malala in the left side of her head; the bullet then

15　traveled down her neck.   Two other girls were also injured in the attack.

Surviving the attack, Malala brought (4)an important symbol with her to the Nobel Prize Award Ceremony in Oslo: the bloody uniform she was wearing when she was shot on the school bus.   "Education went from being a right to being a crime," she said.   "But when my world suddenly changed, my *priorities changed, too.   I had two alternatives.   One was to

20　remain silent and wait to be killed.   And the second was to speak up and then be killed.   I chose the second one.   I decided to speak up."

Malala is committed to an issue that needs attention.   (5)According to research by *UNICEF, over 60 million girls worldwide did not attend school in 2011.   Although there are many reasons for this, including limited resources, a lack of teachers, and family priorities, much of it

25　is still caused by discrimination.   And as Malala's story shows, girls too often face physical violence when they attempt to gain access to education.　　　　(392 words / 甲南大学)

---

5 Taliban[tá:ləbà:n]：パキスタンやアフガニスタンで活動する組織
19 priority[praɪɔ́:rəti]：優先事項
22 UNICEF[jú:nisèf]：ユニセフ、国連児童基金

CAN-DO List 〈知識・技能〉群前置詞、群接続詞について理解できる。
〈思考力・判断力・表現力〉マララさん襲撃事件と、パキスタンの女子教育の現状について理解できる。

1. この英文のタイトルとして最も適当なものを、次の a.～d. から選びなさい。　　　　（5点）

 a．The Life of Malala Yousafzai : Speak Up for Education

 b．Malala Yousafzai and the Taliban : The Battle for Equal Human Rights

 c．Malala Yousafzai : The Last Person to be a Nobel Prize Winner

 d．The Life of Malala Yousafzai : Grow up in Pakistan

精 読問題 もう一度英文を読んで、次の問いに答えなさい。

2. 下線部(1)は具体的に何を「最後にしよう」と述べていますか。日本語で二つ挙げなさい。（各3点）

 ① _____　　② _____

3. 下線部(2)のタリバンという組織は、マララさんが暮らす地域でどのようなことをしていましたか。
日本語で述べなさい。　　　　　　　　　　　　　　　　　　　　　　　　　　　　（4点）

_____

4. 下線部(3)が表す意味として最も適当なものを、次の a.～d. から一つ選びなさい。　　　（4点）

 a．the seat where she was sitting was revealed

 b．the seat which she was taking was retained

 c．the bus which she was taking was disclosed

 d．the place where she was going was decided

5. 下線部(4)は具体的にはどのようなものか、[　　]内に適語を入れ、日本語で答えなさい。　（4点）

[　　　　　　　　　　　　　　　　　　　　　　　　　　]血の付いた制服。

6. 文法 下線部(5)の結果判明したことはどのようなことですか。書き出しに続けて日本語で述べな
さい。　　　　　　　　　　　　　　　　　　　　　　　　　　　　　　　　　（5点）

2011年に_____。

7. 全体把握 本文の内容と合うように、（　　）内に適当な一語を補いなさい。　　（完答各3点）

 (ア) Malala Yousafzai is the (　　　　　　　) person in history to receive a (　　　　　　　)
  (　　　　　　).

 (イ) Malala was shot by a terrorist on the (　　　　　　　) bus on (　　　　　　) 9, 2012.

 (ウ) Malala decided to (　　　　　　) (　　　　　　) even if she might be killed.

 (エ) When girls try to receive their (　　　　　　), they too often (　　　　　　) physical
  (　　　　　　).

Grammar 目標➡7分

1 次の各文の（　）内から適当なほうを選びなさい。 （各1点）

1. I asked some people for directions, but (neither / none) of them were able to help me.
2. John and I couldn't get into the house because (neither / none) of us had a key.
3. Not (all / every) cars have air conditioners.
4. I sometimes go for a walk after lunch, but (always not / not always).
5. I'll have to go shopping.　We have hardly (any / ever) food.
6. I'm almost always at home at night.　I hardly (any / ever) go out.

2 次の各組の文がほぼ同じ意味になるように、（　）内に適語を補いなさい。 （各3点）

1. This teddy bear always reminds me of my happy childhood.
   I never see this teddy bear (　　　　　　　) thinking of my happy childhood.
2. My grandmother always telephones me on my birthday.
   My grandmother never (　　　　　　　) to telephone me on my birthday.
3. The show was not a failure at all; it was a great success.
   The show was (　　　　　　　) from being a failure; it was a great success.
4. Tom never tells a lie.
   Tom is the (　　　　　　　) person to tell a lie.
5. Mary will soon leave the town.
   It won't be long (　　　　　　　) Mary leaves the town.

Writing 目標➡3分

3 （　）内の語を並べかえて英文を完成しなさい。 （各5点）

1. 彼女は10個の帽子をかぶってみたが、どれも魅力的ではなかった。
   She tried on ten hats, but (attractive / of / none / them / were).

   _____

2. どんなことであれ、ミスをしてできるようになる。
   You (anything / cannot / do / learn / to / without) making mistakes.

   _____

3. 貧しいからというそれだけの理由で、人を軽べつすべきではない。
   We ought not to look down on people (are / because / poor / simply / they).

   _____

Listening 目標➡5分　　　テーマ 環境　🔊 32

4 Mayuko の短いスピーチを聞き、二つの空所に入れるのに最も適当なものを、①〜④から一つずつ選びなさい。　　　　　　　　　　　　　　　　　　　　　　　　（各5点）

1．Even after plastics are partially decomposed, they will ⬚ .
  ① stay in the ocean as microplastics　　　② not do harm to marine creatures
  ③ disappear sooner or later　　　　　　　④ stay in the ocean for over 500 years

2．According to Mayuko, we should ⬚ .
  ① say no to using unnecessary plastic products　② use plastic straws when ordering a drink
  ③ be able to decompose plastics in the future　④ not use plastic products at all

Rapid Reading 目標➡5分　　　テーマ 環境　GTEC®

5 ウェブサイトを読み取って、問いに対する答えとして最も適当なものを一つずつ選びなさい。
（各5点）

How to Reduce Plastic Waste in the Oceans

500 million tons of plastic are produced annually all over the world.

In 2020 we will generate **900% more** plastic than in 1980.

There are already more than **150 million** tons of plastic waste in the oceans.

By 2050 the oceans could contain more plastic than fish.

In fact, in 2021 the EU will ban the sale of single-use plastics such as drinking straws, cutlery or cotton buds within its borders.　This is one of the measures being introduced by many governments in the world in order to reduce the negative effects caused by the plastic waste as it has now become a serious headache for the planet.

How Long Does It Take for Single-use Plastics to Biologically Decompose?

・When we use single-use plastic products, their average useful life is 12 to 15 minutes, and yet it is estimated that we have to wait for 500 years until they disappear from the oceans.　Plastic bottles stay in the sea for 500 years, plastic bags 400 years, toothbrushes 500 years, and drinking straws 200 years.

・Rather than by bacteria, plastic is broken down through a process called "photodegradation" whereby UV radiation from the sun breaks down the plastic into smaller pieces over time.

・When plastic eventually breaks down into smaller particles called "microplastics," these can be eaten by fish —— and end up in food eaten by humans.　This may lead to another problem; therefore, the best solution for plastic waste is to avoid using single-use plastic products.　In addition, the companies producing them should change to non-plastic products.

1．Which of the following statements is true?
  ① 500 million tons of plastic wastes were produced in 2020.
  ② Plastic wastes in the oceans eventually become microplastics and cause other problems.
  ③ The average useful life of single-use plastic products is said to be about 400 to 500 years.
  ④ We should not avoid using single-use plastic products.

2．Why did the EU decide to ban the sale of single-use plastics in 2021?
  ① A lot of governments including the EU are trying to solve the plastic waste problems.
  ② UV radiation from the sun breaks down the plastic into smaller pieces over time.
  ③ By 2050, it is estimated that we will have more plastic waste in the oceans than fish.
  ④ More and more governments are promoting their policies to improve the image of plastic ocean pollution.

速 読問題　次の英文を2.5分で読んで、1. の問いに答えなさい。

At the end of 2017, China announced that it would no longer receive plastic waste from other countries, its waste systems no longer able to deal with plastic coming from elsewhere given increased rates of domestic plastic production. (1)European and North American countries now have to search for new destinations for their waste. One possible outcome of this is that waste from the West could end up maxing out the capacity of infrastructure in Southeast Asia, making it even harder for some of these countries to deal with the problems arising from their own plastic use.

This is why attempts to blame other countries for letting more plastic get into the ocean should be viewed with *scepticism. Although it may technically be the case, there is likely to be (2)a variety of factors such as waste exports, lack of safe drinking water requiring plastic bottles, and lack of investment by companies producing the plastic in the first place that are making it nearly impossible for them to deal effectively with the amount of waste being produced.

One such example is the Philippines which, according to a 2015 study published in *Science*, is the third worst polluter of the oceans. However, (3)a 2017 cleanup effort in Manila Bay collected 54,620 pieces of plastic, documenting where possible the brand of every item they collected. Out of the top five worst offending companies, three are well-known multinational corporations: Unilever, Nestlé and Procter & Gamble. These are companies that in some countries are going to great lengths to demonstrate their *sustainability credentials; however, clearly they are still a major part of the environmental problem on the other side of the world.

One of the biggest issues with these consumer goods companies is their production of *sachets. (4)Sachets allow for very small quantities of liquids to be packaged. Unfortunately, these sachets are non-recyclable and are sold in huge quantities; this means that they are winding up on the beaches across Southeast Asia as people cannot easily dispose of them responsibly. (5)Countries in Southeast Asia are often blamed for being *disproportionately responsible for the plastic pollution crisis; however, the *culpability of companies that are irresponsibly producing plastic products is rarely discussed.

(365 words ／ 慶應義塾大学)

---

⁹scepticism[sképtɪsìz(ə)m]：懐疑的な態度、疑い　　¹⁸sustainability credential：環境に配慮している証明
²¹sachet[sæʃéɪ]：小袋　　²⁴disproportionately[dìsprəpɔ́ːrʃ(ə)nətli]：不釣り合いに
²⁵culpability[kʌ̀lpəbíləti]：過失、責任

CAN-DO List
☐ 🔍 〈知識・技能〉否定語・部分否定・準否定語・二重否定・否定語を含まない否定について理解できる。
☐ 📖 〈思考力・判断力・表現力〉世界のプラスチックごみ問題の現状について理解できる。

1. この英文のタイトルとして最も適当なものを、次の a.～ d. から選びなさい。　　　　（5点）

   a. Who Should Take the Responsibility for Their Own Plastic Waste?

   b. Which Country Produces the Most Plastic Waste in the World?

   c. How Should We Deal with the Plastic Waste in Southeast Asia?

   d. What Is Needed to Decrease the Amount of Plastic Waste in Europe and the U.S.?

精 読問題 もう一度英文を読んで、次の問いに答えなさい。

2. 下線部(1)の状況が生じた理由を、40字程度の日本語で述べなさい。　　　　（7点）

_____

3. 下線部(2)の具体例を三つ日本語で簡単に箇条書きしなさい。　　　　（各3点）

_____

_____

4. 下線部(3)の清掃活動の際、プラスチック回収のほかにどのようなことを行ったか、日本語で答えなさい。　　　　（6点）

_____

5. 下線部(4)が環境問題を引き起こす理由はどのようなものか、日本語で説明しなさい。　　　　（6点）

_____

6. 文法 下線部(5)と対照的な内容となっている箇所について、日本語で説明しなさい。　　　　（6点）

_____

7. 全体把握 本文の内容と合っているものにはT、合っていないものにはFと答えなさい。 （各1点）

   (ア) At the end of 2017, China said that it was impossible for them to deal with plastic waste from other countries. 　　　　（　　）

   (イ) Some European countries have difficulty dealing with the problems from their own plastic use. 　　　　（　　）

   (ウ) Doubts should be cast on the view that other countries should be responsible for allowing more plastic to be thrown away into the oceans. 　　　　（　　）

   (エ) According to a study in *Science* published in 2015, the Philippines is the worst country at polluting the oceans. 　　　　（　　）

   (オ) Unilever, Nestlé and Procter & Gamble are well-known multinational corporations but they are also the cause of the environmental problems on the other side of the world. 　　　　（　　）

Grammar 目標➡ 7分

1 次の各文の（　）内に入れるのに最も適当なものを選び、記号を補いなさい。 （各2点）

1. It is not what we eat but what we digest (　　　) makes us strong.
   a. that　　　　　b. what　　　　　c. where　　　　　d. how

2. It wasn't until I went to work (　　　) I discovered how important school is.
   a. before　　　　b. that　　　　　c. then　　　　　d. when

3. What (　　　) did you go to such a dangerous place for?
   a. in the earth　　b. in world　　　c. on earth　　　d. on the world

4. The students did not understand that lecture in the (　　　).
   a. least　　　　　b. less　　　　　c. little　　　　　d. few

5. Last year I visited Canada, and (　　　).
   a. so did Mary　　b. so Mary did　c. so Mary was　d. so was Mary

6. Dogs aren't allowed on the airplane. (　　　).
   a. So are cats　　b. Cats aren't too　c. Either aren't cats　d. Neither are cats

7. Not until he was five (　　　) to ride a bicycle.
   a. John did start　b. John did not start　c. did John start　d. did John not start

8. Hardly (　　　) the building when the fire broke out.
   a. I had left　　　b. have I left　　c. had I left　　d. I left

9. (　　　) not been for your help, I would have failed.
   a. Had there　　　b. Had it　　　c. Were it　　　d. Has it

Writing 目標➡ 3分

2 1.～3. は（　）内の語句を並べかえなさい。4.、5. は英訳しなさい。

（1～3：各4点／4、5：各5点）

1. No, Bill was second in the race. It (came / first / his brother Jim / that / was).

   _____

2. そのいすは修理しなければいけない。それに、ぼくが今腰かけているいすもだ。
   That chair needs repairing, and so (does / I'm / on / sitting / the one).

   _____

3. 彼が訪ねて来てくれるなんて夢にも思わなかった。
   Never (come / see / he / me / dream / and / would / I / did).

   _____

4. ぼくが会いたかったのはメアリーではなくてあなただったのです。
   It was _____.

5. 再び歩けるようになるには、彼は手術を受けるしかありません。
   Only after an operation _____.

3 長めの会話を一つ聞き、問いの答えとして最も適当なものを一つずつ選びなさい。　（各5点）

1. Which activity are the speakers likely to give up?

　① Visit to a history museum.　　② Boat trip around the canal.

　③ Sightseeing cruise.　　④ Walking around the Chinatown.

2. How long is the speakers' free time?

　① About one hour.　　② About one and a half hours.

　③ About two hours.　　④ About two and a half hours.

Rapid Reading　　目標➡5分　　　テーマ　空港

4 掲示を読み取って、問いに対する答えとして最も適当なものを一つずつ選びなさい。　（各5点）

| ✈ DEPARTURE | | | | | 23:30 now |
TIME	TO	FLIGHT	GATE	ETD	REMARK
23:55	Hong Kong	UO623	107	23:20	DEPARTED
0:05	Bangkok	JL33	113		FINAL CALL
0:05	Singapore	JL35	112		FINAL CALL
0:05	Kuala Lumpur	NH885	110		FINAL CALL
0:10	Singapore	NH843	108A	0:20	BOARDING
0:20	Bangkok	TG661	147		BOARDING
0:30	Dubai	EK313	145	1:30	DELAYED
0:30	Bangkok	NH849	109		BOARDING
0:35	Paris (CDG)	AF293	142	0:20	RESCHEDULED
0:55	Frankfurt	NH203	111		CLOSED
0:55	Hong Kong	NH82	106A		CLOSED
1:10	Hong Kong	KA397	141		CLOSED

1. According to this flight schedule, how many flights will depart between midnight and 1 o'clock?

　① 7 flights.　　② 8 flights.　　③ 9 flights.　　④ 10 flights.

2. Which of the following statements is true?

　① Flight UO623 to Hong Kong has not departed yet.

　② The next flight to Hong Kong will depart in 1 hour and 40 minutes.

　③ Flight EK313 to Dubai, scheduled to depart at 0:30 a.m., will be delayed for 1 hour.

　④ Flight AF293 to Paris, scheduled to depart at 0:35 a.m., will depart on time.

CAN-DO List　☐ 🎧 〈思考力・判断力・表現力〉対話を聞いて、内容を正しく聞き分けることができる。　　**Lesson 14**　| 57

☐ 📋 〈思考力・判断力・表現力〉掲示から、必要な情報を読み取ることができる。

Reading

目標➡20分　　　　　　　文法項目 倒置　テーマ 文化　　🔊 35

速読問題 次の英文を2.5分で読んで、1. の問いに答えなさい。

In Somalia, (1)we lived the way our ancestors had for thousands of years; nothing had changed dramatically for us.　As *nomads we did not live with electricity, telephones, or automobiles, much less computers, television, or space travel.　These facts, combined with our emphasis on living in the present, gave us a much different perspective on time than the one that dominates the Western world.

Like the rest of my family, I have no idea how old I am; I can only guess.　A baby who is born in my country has little guarantee of being alive one year later, so the concept of tracking birthdays does not retain the same importance.　When I was a child, we lived without the artificial time constructions of schedules, clocks, and calendars.　(2)Instead, we lived by the seasons and the sun, (3)planning our day based on the span of daylight available.　We told time by using the sun.　If my shadow was on the west side, it was morning; when it moved directly underneath me, it was noon.　When my shadow crossed to the other side, it was afternoon. As the sun moved lower, shadows of things grew longer and (4)so did my shadow——my cue to start heading home before dark.

(5)When we got up in the morning, we decided what we'd do that day, then did that task the best we could until we finished or the sky grew too dark for us to see.　There was no such notion of getting up and having your day all planned out for you.　In New York, people frequently take out their *datebooks and ask, "Are you free for lunch on the fourteenth——or what about the fifteenth?"　I respond with "Why don't you call me the day before you want to meet up?"　No matter how many times I write down appointments, I can't get used to (6)the idea.　When I first came to London, I was confused by the connection between people staring at their wrist, then crying, "I've got to dash!"　I felt like everyone was rushing everywhere, every action was timed.　In Africa there was no hurry, no stress.　African time is very, very slow, very calm.　If you say, "I'll see you tomorrow around noon," that means about four or five o'clock.　And today I still refuse to wear a watch.

(392 words / 日本福祉大学)

---

² nomad [nóʊmæd]：遊牧民　　¹⁸ datebook [déɪtbʊ̀k]：手帳

CAN-DO List　□ 🔍 〈知識・技能〉強調表現・倒置について理解できる。
　　　　　　　　□ 💭 〈思考力・判断力・表現力〉時間に束縛されないソマリアの生活様式について理解できる。

1. この英文は全体として何について述べていますか。次の a.～ d. から選びなさい。　　（5点）

    a. 明日という未来も保証されていない生活

    b. 現代文明の恩恵を受けられないでいる生活

    c. 時間に支配されない生活

    d. 時の流れが停止している生活

精 読問題 もう一度英文を読んで、次の問いに答えなさい。

2. 下線部(1)の具体的な内容を、日本語で説明しなさい。　　（4点）

_____

3. 下線部(2)は何をしないでということか、日本語で説明しなさい。　　（4点）

_____

4. 下線部(3)の意味として最も適当なものを a.～ d. から一つ選びなさい。　　（2点）

    a. あらかじめ決めていたスケジュールにしたがって一日の計画を立てる。

    b. その日の活動可能な昼の長さにしたがって一日の計画を立てる。

    c. その日の昼の長さとは関係なく自分の思い通りに一日の計画を立てる。

    d. その日の空模様を見極めて一日の計画を立てる。

5. 文法 下線部(4)を倒置構文を用いないで書きなさい。　　（3点）

   and _____

6. 下線部(5)と対照的な内容を表している箇所を、本文中から抜き出しなさい。　　（4点）

_____

7. 下線部(6)の具体的な内容を、日本語で簡単に説明しなさい。　　（4点）

8. 全体把握 本文の内容と合うように、（　　）内に適当な一語を補いなさい。　　（各2点）

  (ア) People in Somalia have a very unique way of thinking about (　　　　　　).

  (イ) They don't know exactly how old they are, because they don't know their (　　　　　　).

  (ウ) A baby who is born in Somalia (　　　　　　) not be alive one year later.

  (エ) As the sun got lower, the author's shadow grew (　　　　　). It was (　　　　　) for her to start for home.

  (オ) "Are you free for lunch on the fourteenth?" means "(　　　　　) don't we meet up for lunch on the fourteenth?"

  (カ) When the author first came to London, she didn't know that people had a watch on their (　　　　　　).

  (キ) Today the author still doesn't carry a (　　　　　　).

Lesson 15 特殊構文③

Grammar 目標➡7分

1 次の各文の（　　）内に下記の語群から適語を選んで補いなさい。　(各2点)

1. The singer made her first (　　　　　) in a concert in San Francisco.
2. John could give no (　　　　　) for being late.
3. My (　　　　　) to follow his advice made him upset.
4. The sudden (　　　　　) of their pet dog was a great shock to them.
5. I believe that (　　　　　) of others is the base of good manners.

【appearance / consideration / death / explanation / refusal】

2 次の各組の文がほぼ同じ意味になるように、（　　）内に適語を補いなさい。　(各3点)

1. How fluently she speaks English!
   What a fluent (　　　　　) of English she is!
2. My mother was happy to hear the news.
   The (　　　　　) (　　　　　) my mother happy.
3. Why did he leave this town?
   What (　　　　　) (　　　　　) leave this town?
4. After a few minutes' walk, we came to the park.
   A few minutes' walk (　　　　　) (　　　　　) to the park.
5. Since he knew Spanish, we could travel through Spain comfortably.
   His (　　　　　) of Spanish enabled us to travel through Spain comfortably.

Writing 目標➡3分

3 1.～3. は（　　）内の語句を並べかえなさい。4.、5. は英訳しなさい。

(1～3：各3点／4、5：各5点)

1. 私は子供のころ漢字を覚えるのが遅かった。
   I (learner / when / I / was / Kanji / of / a / slow) was a child.

   _____

2. I'll have (a / a mechanic / look / to get / to have) at my car.　It isn't working properly.

   _____

3. The use (computers / has / it / made / of / possible) for more people to work from home.

   _____

4. この薬を飲めば2、3時間で気分がよくなるでしょう。
   This medicine _____ _____.

5. きみはどうしてその会社で働く決心をしたのですか。
   What _____?

　CAN-DO List　□ 🔎　〈知識・技能〉名詞構文・無生物主語構文を適切に活用できる。

Listening

目標→5分 | テーマ 買い物 | 共通テスト | 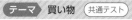 36

4 英文を聞き、□1□〜□4□の空所に合うものを①〜④から一つずつ選びなさい。 (各2点)

ネットショッピングを利用する理由やネットショッピングのメリット

	日本	米国	英国	ドイツ	韓国	中国
□1□	68.1	67.4	62.3	56.0	78.0	53.7
24時間いつでも買い物ができる	62.8	68.9	68.7	56.5	76.5	61.1
□2□	54.6	47.1	52.9	49.0	76.1	67.6
実店舗よりも品揃えが豊富	40.3	48.0	49.2	50.6	49.9	57.8
実店舗に行く時間を節約できる	36.5	51.0	51.2	32.3	59.5	52.3
検索機能等によって買いたいものを探す時間を節約できる	24.5	39.7	41.5	25.1	55.4	35.9
対面での接客を省略できる	13.1	28.3	22.8	13.8	28.0	16.1
□3□	23.8	38.5	36.9	31.3	43.6	41.4
購入履歴から欲しいものを提示してくれる	6.6	16.7	13.0	3.7	17.5	26.2
□4□	33.9	21.5	44.8	23.0	58.3	28.6
ポイント	21.9	9.9	8.7	7.1	40.2	18.4

□1□ (　) 　　□2□ (　) 　　□3□ (　) 　　□4□ (　)

① 実店舗に出向かなくても買い物ができる

② 実店舗よりも安く買える

③ ショッピングサイトのレビューを参照して購入する

④ 持ち帰るのが重いものを手軽に買える

Rapid Reading

目標→5分 | テーマ 買い物

5 英文を読んで、問いに対する答えとして最も適当なものを一つずつ選びなさい。 (各5点)

　When you go shopping at an actual store, you might imagine that the only benefit is that you can buy something you need or want. This means that you can receive what you want on the spot. Actually, it seems that there is also a secondary benefit: You see and talk to various people as you shop, so you feel less lonely.

　Today, Internet shopping is becoming more common because online shoppers enjoy the convenience, but they tend to buy more things they don't need. Some point out that this is because they do not talk to anyone when shopping online. Communication with others seems to have something to do with our decision-making processes.

1. What is the benefit of shopping at an actual store?

　① You can get what you want or need on the spot.

　② You can get an extra discount by talking to a store clerk.

　③ You do not have to talk to other people at a store.

　④ You can decide what you want or need before going shopping.

2. What is suggested about Internet shopping?

　① You are likely to spend less money.

　② You tend to buy unnecessary things.

　③ You often cancel your order.

　④ You can talk to a store clerk.

Reading   目標➡20分   文法項目 名詞構文・無生物主語構文   テーマ 買い物   37

速 読問題 次の英文を2.5分で読んで、1. の問いに答えなさい。

It's 6:15 on a Friday evening in the Lincoln Mall in Chicago.   Holidays are coming up and it is time to grab some last-minute bargains, but tonight the sound of shopping is nowhere to be heard. The shop spaces, once full of goods and people, are now open and empty.   All of this is because of something that is becoming more and more common across America today; (1)the dead mall.

5   Building a new shopping mall is expensive, but (2)this is only part of the cost.   The owners then need to advertise and attract retail stores of all types, from fashion to food.   Electricity, water and gas are always being used and there are other expenses such as taxes and legal fees that can be much higher than the owners of the mall might expect.   It can be hard for them to make a profit, even in an area with lots of people wanting to shop.

10   One key to the success of a shopping mall is something called (3)an "anchor store."   This is a huge, popular store such as a department store or supermarket, owned by a well-known company like Walmart.   People come to the mall to buy something from these places, then visit the rest of the shops while they are there.   However, if an anchor store closes down, then the whole mall often loses most of its customers.   The other, smaller shops cannot survive

15 there and leave, one by one.   When nobody is left, the mall is "dead."

(4)Anchor stores, along with smaller shops, are having a much more difficult time than they used to in America.   Part of the reason for this is the rise of Internet shopping, through companies such as Amazon.   Many customers wonder why they should go to a physical store when they can buy the same goods more cheaply online and have them delivered directly to

20 their homes.   This means that more and more of these large stores are closing down, so the number of dead malls across America is only likely to increase in the coming years.

Sometimes, these huge, abandoned spaces can successfully be turned into something else. A few have been converted into churches, some have become public housing and others have been turned into office spaces and technology centers.   However, rebuilding is a financial risk

25 and can require the owners to make a great amount of effort, (5)so often they simply abandon the space, leaving nothing but a vast, crumbling roadside monument to a changing way of life.

(418 words / 成蹊大学)

CAN-DO List   ☐ 〈知識・技能〉名詞構文・無生物主語構文について理解できる。
☐ 〈思考力・判断力・表現力〉オンラインショッピングのもたらす未来図について理解できる。

1. この英文のタイトルとして最も適当なものを、次の a.～ d.から選びなさい。　　　　　（5点）

 a．What Dead Malls Will Become

 b．Dead Malls and the Plans for Rebuilding

 c．Shopping Malls and Internet Shopping

 d．The History of Physical Stores

精 読問題 もう一度英文を読んで、次の問いに答えなさい。

2. 下線部(1)の the dead mall とはどのような状態のモールか、[　　]内に適語を入れて日本文を完成しなさい。　　　　　（5点）

 かつては商品や人々で溢れていた空間が[　　　　　　　　　　　　　　　　　]状態のモール。

3. 下線部(2)について、ショッピングモールの建設費以外の費用について、本文の内容を以下の[　　]内に適語を入れてまとめなさい。　　　　　（各2点）

 モールのオーナーが広告を出し、[①　　　　　　　　　　　　　　　]あらゆる種類の小売店を[②　　　　　　　]必要がある。[③　　　　　　　]は常に使用され、[④　　　　　　　]や弁護士費用といったような出費はオーナーが[⑤　　　　　　　]よりも高額になる。

4. 文法 下線部(3)はどのような店舗ですか。[　　]内に適語を入れ、日本語で説明しなさい。

 （各2点）

 ウォルマートのような[①　　　　　　　]によって所有された[②　　　　　　　　　　]のような巨大で人気のある店舗。

5. 下線部(4)の状況になっている理由を、 a.～ d.から一つ選びなさい。　　　　　（5点）

 a．Internet shopping is becoming more and more popular.

 b．More and more larger stores are closing down.

 c．More and more people are going to physical stores.

 d．More people wonder why they should use Internet shopping.

6. 文法 下線部(5)の理由を、日本語で説明しなさい。　　　　　（5点）

7. 全体把握 本文の内容と合うように、（　　）内に適当な一語を補いなさい。　　　　　（各1点）

 (ア) In the dead mall, the (　　　　　　　) of shopping cannot be heard.

 (イ) Because of a lot of (　　　　　　　), it is hard for the mall owners to make a profit.

 (ウ) More and more (　　　　　　　) shops are closing down because of the rise of Internet shopping.

 (エ) The (　　　　　　) shopping malls can be turned into something else, such as churches, public housing, office spaces or technology centers.

Sources

■Listening

Lesson 10（グラフ）

令和元年度(年度)空港別順位表(国土交通省)のデータをもとに作成

Lesson 15（グラフ）

IoT 時代における新たな ICT への各国ユーザーの意識の分析等に関する調査結果(総務省：平成28年)のデータをもとに作成

■Rapid Reading

Lesson 5（グラフ）

世界子供白書2016(ユニセフ)のデータをもとに作成

■Reading

Lesson 4

Prism Reading Level 2, Lida Baker, Carolyn Westbrook. Reproduced with permission of Cambridge University Press through PLSclear.

Lesson 7

J B Priestley, English Journey, Great Northern Books Ltd, 2009

Lesson 8

Peter Trudgill, The Dialects of England, John Wiley and Sons, 1999

Lesson 10

The Japan Times（2019年 1 月 4 日掲載　The Japan Times Alpha）